The Pioneers

&

Fast in the Ice

THE PIONEERS *Reprinted from the 1872 Classic by R.M. Ballantyne*
FAST IN THE ICE *Reprinted from the 1882 Classic by R.M. Ballantyne*

SECOND PRINTING

"Where there is no vision, the people perish."

www.visionforum.com

ISBN-10 1-934554-22-7
ISBN-13 978-1-934554-22-7

The cloth covers in this series are color-coded to represent the geographic region of each story. The regions and their respective colors are as follows:

NORTH AMERICA—*Forest Green*	SOUTH AMERICA—*Wheat*
SOUTH PACIFIC—*Light Blue*	ARCTIC REGIONS—*Grey*
EUROPE—*Navy Blue*	AFRICA—*Sienna*
ASIA—*Red*	

PRINTED IN THE UNITED STATES OF AMERICA

 The "Scotch Thistle," the floral emblem of Scotland, serves as the emblem of the R.M. Ballantyne Series published by Vision Forum.

ADDITIONAL TITLES IN VISION FORUM'S
R.M. BALLANTYNE SERIES

The Coral Island: A Tale of the Pacific Ocean

The Gorilla Hunters: A Tale of the Wilds of Africa

Hunted and Harried: A Tale of the Scottish Covenanters

Martin Rattler: Adventures of a Boy in the Forests of Brazil

The Cannibal Island: Captain Cook's Adventures in the South Seas

Fighting the Flames: The London Fire Brigade, and How it Worked

The Dog Crusoe: A Story of Adventure in the Western Prairies

Gascoyne, The Sandal-wood Trader: A Tale of the Pacific

The Island Queen: Dethroned by Fire and Water

Blue Lights, or Hot Work in the Soudan

The Pirate City: An Algerine Tale

Red Rooney, or The Last of the Crew

Ungava: A Tale of the Esquimaux Land

Post Haste: A Tale of Her Majesty's Mails

Deep Down: A Tale of the Cornish Mines

The Lonely Island: The Refuge of the Mutineers

The Young Fur Traders: A Tale of the Far North

The Giant of the North: Pokings Round the Pole

The Norsemen in the West, or America before Columbus

A WILD GOOSE CHASE—Page 69

The Pioneers

A Tale of the Western Wilderness

by

R.M. BALLANTYNE

Author of
Fast In The Ice, Gascoyne,
Fighting the Whales, etc., etc.

THE VISION FORUM, INC.
San Antonio, Texas

PREFACE

SIR ALEXANDER Mackenzie was one of the most energetic and successful of the discoverers who have traversed the vast wilderness of British America. He did his work single-handed, with slender means, and slight encouragement, at a time when discovery was rare and the country almost *terra incognita*. The long and difficult route, so recently traversed by the Red River Expedition, was, to Sir Alexander, but the small beginning of his far-reaching travels. He traced the great river which bears his name to its outlet in the Polar Sea, and was the first to cross the Rocky Mountains in those latitudes and descend to the Pacific ocean.

Being a man of action, and not particularly enamoured of the pen, his journal [For a sight of which apply to the British Museum, London, or the Advocates' Library, Edinburgh]—full though it be of important and most interesting facts—is a bare and unadorned though valuable record of progress made, of work done, which is unsuited to juvenile minds, besides being bulky and scarce.

Having spent some years in Rupert's Land, and seen something of Red Indian and fur trading life, I have ventured to weave the incidents of Sir Alexander's narratives into a story which, it is hoped, may prove interesting to the young—perchance, also, to the old.

I take this opportunity of acknowledging myself deeply indebted to Sir Alexander's daughter, Miss Mackenzie, and to his two sons, for kindly placing at my disposal all the information in their possession.

R.M.B.

EDINBURGH, 1872.

CONTENTS

Chapter I

"The world is round," said somebody in ancient times to somebody else.

"Not at all; it is flat—flat as a pancake," replied somebody else to somebody; "and if you were to travel far enough, you might get to the end of it and tumble over the edge, if so disposed."

Ever since the commencement of this early geographical controversy, men have been labouring with more or less energy and success to ascertain the form and character of the earth; a grand, glorious labour it has been; resulting in blessings innumerable to mankind, both spiritual and temporal.

We have heard some people object to geographical discovery, especially in the inclement parts of the earth, on the ground that it could be of no use, and involved great risk to life and limb. "Of no use!" Who can tell what discoveries shall be useful and what useless? "The works of God are great, sought out of all those that have pleasure therein," saith the Scripture. There is no reference here to usefulness, but the searching out of God's works, without limitation, is authorised; and those who "take pleasure therein," will be content to leave the result of their labours in the hands of Him who sent them forth. As to "risk," why, a carpenter cannot ascend to the top of a house to put the rafters thereon without risk; a chemist cannot investigate the properties of certain fumes without risk; you cannot even eat your dinner without risk. Only this are we sure of that, if man had never undertaken labour except when such was obviously useful and devoid of risk, the world would still be in the darkness of the Middle Ages.

Reuben Guff held these sentiments, or something like them; and Reuben was a man who had seen a great deal of life in his day, although at the time we introduce him to public notice he had not lived more than six-and-thirty summers. He was a bronzed, stalwart Canadian. His father had been Scotch, his mother of French extraction; and Reuben possessed the dogged resolution of the Scot with the vivacity of the Frenchman. In regard to his tastes and occupation we shall let him speak for himself.

Sitting under a pine-tree, in the wild wilderness that lies to the north of Canada with the drumstick of a goose in one hand and a scalping-knife in the other; with a log-fire in front of him, and his son, a stripling of sixteen, by his side, he delivered himself of the following sentiments—

"I tell 'ee what it is, Lawrence," (the lad was named after the great river on the banks of which he had been reared), "I was born to be a pioneer. Ever since I was the height of a three-fut rule, I've had a skunner at the settlements and a love for the wilderness that I couldn't overcome nohow. Moreover, I wouldn't overcome it if I could, for it's my opinion that He who made us knows what He wants us to do, an' has given us sitch feelin's and inclinations as will lead us to do it, if we don't run mad after notions of our own, as the folk in the settlements are raither apt to do."

Here some of the "notions" referred to appeared to tickle the fancy of the backwoodsman, for he paused to indulge in a quiet chuckle which wrinkled up all the lines of good-humour and fun in his rough countenance. After applying himself for a few seconds with much energy to the drumstick,—he resumed his discourse in a slow, deliberate style of speech which was peculiar to him—

"Yes, Lawrence, my lad, I've made it my business ever since I was fifteen to explore this here wilderness, livin' by my gun and guidin' the furtraders on their v'yages, or consorting with the Injins, as you know very well; and, now that we've come to the big lake it is needful to tell 'ee that I'm still bent on followin' out my callin'. I'm goin' away to the nor'ard to explore, and you'll have to make up your mind tonight whether you will be my steersman or whether I'm to lay that dooty on Swiftarrow. I needn't say which I'd like best."

The hunter finished the drumstick at this point, threw the bone into the fire, lit his pipe, and awaited his son's answer in silence.

But the son appeared to be in no hurry to reply;

for, after giving his father a glance and nod, which were meant to say, "I hear and I'll consider, but I'm too much engaged just now to speak," he continued his occupation of devouring venison steaks, the sauce to which was evidently hunger.

Having finished his supper and lighted his pipe he became more communicative.

"Father," he said, "you have always advised me to think well before speaking."

"I have, lad; it's the natur,' of our forefathers an' a very good natur' too. I'd be sorry to see it go out of the family."

"Well, then; I've thought my best about goin' with 'ee on this trip," returned the youth, "an' I've resolved to go on one condition—that Swiftarrow goes with us."

"Why so, my son? we don't need him."

"Perhaps not, but I like him; for he has taught me all that I know of woodcraft, and I'm certain that if you and I both leave him, he'll be sure to return to the new settlement at the south end of Ontario, and you know what the end of that would be."

"Death by drinkin'," replied Reuben Guff shaking

his head slowly, while he watched the upward flight of a ring of white smoke that had just issued from his lips.

"Well, I won't leave him to that," continued the youth, with sudden energy of manner and look, "as long as my name is Lawrence. You know that nothin' would please me more than goin' to explore the wilderness with you, Father; but if Swiftarrow is to be left behind, there shall be no pioneering for me. Besides, three are better than two on such a trip, and the Injin will be sure to keep the pot full, no matter what sort o' country we may have to pass through, for he's a dead shot wi' the gun as well as wi' the bow."

"I daresay you're right, lad," replied Reuben, in a tone of one who muses. "There's room in the canoe for three, and it's not unlikely that the Injin would go south to the settlement, for he is a lonely man since his poor mother died. I do believe that it was nothin' but his extraor'nar' love for that old 'ooman that kep' him from goin' to the dogs. Leastwise it was that kep' him from goin' to the settlement, which is much the same thing, for Swiftarrow can't resist firewater. Yes, lad, you're right—so we'll take him with us. As you say, three are better than two on such a v'yage."

Some weeks after the foregoing conversation the pioneers arrived at the northern end of that great inland sea, Lake Superior, which, being upwards of four hundred miles long, and one hundred and seventy-five miles broad, presents many of the features of the Ocean itself. This end of the lake was, at the time we write of, and still is, an absolute wilderness, inhabited only by scattered tribes of Indians, and almost untouched by the hand of the white man, save at one spot, where the furtraders had planted an isolated establishment. At this point in the wild woods the representatives of the furtraders of Canada were wont to congregate for the settlement of their affairs in the spring of every year, and from this point also trading-parties were despatched in canoes into the still more remote parts of the great northern wilderness, whence they returned with rich cargoes of furs received from the "red men" in exchange for powder and shot, guns, hatchets, knives, cloth, twine, fish hooks, and such articles as were suited to the tastes and wants of a primitive and wandering people.

Here Reuben Guff and his son found Swiftarrow,

as they had expected, and proposed to him that he should accompany them on their voyage north,—a proposal which he accepted with pleasure,—for the strong-boned Indian had an adventurous spirit as well as a healthy frame.

Swiftarrow was a brave and powerful Indian, and was esteemed one of the best hunters of his tribe; but no one seeing him in camp in a quiescent state would have thought him to be possessed of much energy, for he was slow and deliberate in his movements, and withal had a lazy look about his eyes. But the sight of a bear or moose deer had the effect of waking him up in a way that caused his dark eyes to flash and his large frame to move with cat-like activity.

When Reuben Guff discovered him on the shore of Lake Superior, he was seated at the door of his skin lodge, anointing his hair, which was long and black, with bear's grease the "genuine article," without even the admixture of a drop of scent!—so pure, in fact, that the Indian basted his steaks and anointed his hair with grease from the same box.

"Hallo! Swiftarrow," exclaimed Reuben, as he sauntered up to the savage, with his gun on his shoulder, "ye seem to be beautifyin' yerself today—not goin' to get married, eh?"

Swiftarrow, whose long hair hung over his face like a glossy curtain, tossed aside his locks and gazed earnestly at the hunter. A slight smile and a pleasant gleam lighted up his dark countenance as he wiped his greasy right hand on his legging and extended it, exclaiming, "watchee!" by which he meant, what cheer?

"What cheer? what cheer?" replied Reuben, with a broad but quiet grin, as he shook his friend's hand heartily.

Each man understood the other's language perfectly; but each appeared to prefer to talk in his own tongue; for while Reuben addressed the red man in English, Swiftarrow replied in Indian. This had been an understood arrangement between them ever since the time when, as lads, they had first met and formed a close friendship, on the shores of Lake Huron.

"Is my brother's trail to be through the woods or on the waters? Does he go hunting or trading?" inquired the Indian, after the first salutations were over.

"Well, I may say that I'm neither goin' a-huntin' or

tradin' here, fill yer pipe wi' baccy from my pouch; it's better than yours, I'll be bound. In a manner, too, I'm goin' both to hunt an' trade in a small way; but my main business on this trip is to be diskivery."

The Indian uttered a sound, which meant that he did not understand.

"I'm goin' to sarch out new lands," explained Reuben, "away to the far north. I've heard it said by Injins that have wandered to the nor'ard that they've met in with redskins, who said that there is a big river flowin' out o' a great lake in the direction o' the north pole, an' that it runs into the sea there. They may be tellin' truth, or they may be tellin' lies; I dun know; anyhow, I'm koorious to know somethin' about it, so I'm goin' north to see for myself, and I've comed to ask if Swiftarrow will go with me."

The hunter paused, but the Indian remained silently smoking his long stone-headed pipe, or calumet, with a countenance so grave and expressionless, that no idea of his sentiments could be gathered from it. After a brief pause, Reuben continued,

"It won't be altogether a trip of diskivery neither, for I've got some bales of goods with me, and as we go in a small birch canoe, we'll travel light; but I hope to come back sunk to the gunwale with furs, for the redskins of the far north are like enough to have plenty of pelts, and they won't ask much for them. As to grub, you and I could manage to supply ourselves wi' lots o' that anywheres, and I've got plenty of powder and lead. Moreover, my boy Lawrence is goin' with me."

During the foregoing remarks, the Indian's countenance betrayed no sign of feeling until the name of Lawrence was mentioned, when a gleam of satisfaction shot from his eyes. Removing the pipe from his lips, he puffed a volume of smoke through his nostrils, and said—

"Swiftarrow will go."

Backwoodsmen seldom take long to mature their plans, and are generally prompt to carry them into execution. Two days after the brief conversation above narrated, the three friends pushed off in their little birchbark canoe and paddled up the stream which leads to the Kakabeka Falls on the Kamenistaquoia River. Surmounting this obstacle by the simple process of carrying the canoe and her lading past the falls by land, and relaunching on the still water above, they continued their voyage day by day, encamping under the trees by night, until they had penetrated far and deep into the heart of the northern wilderness, and had even passed beyond the most distant establishments of the adventurous furtraders.

The world of forest, swamp, lake, and river, that still, however, lay between them and the land which they sought to reach, was very wide. Weeks, and even months, would certainly elapse before they could hope to approach it; one day, therefore, they buried their goods and stores in a convenient place, intending to dig them up on their return, and meanwhile turned aside into a country which promised to afford them a good supply of fresh provisions for the voyage north.

Here an adventure befell them which brought their voyage of discovery, at that time, to an abrupt close.

Chapter II

"Ho!" ejaculated Swiftarrow.

"Smoke!" exclaimed Reuben Guff.

Both men spoke at the same moment,—their discovery having been simultaneous. At the same time Lawrence pointed with the blade of his paddle to a thin line of smoke which rose above the treetops into the blue sky, and was faithfully mirrored in the lake on which they floated.

"Injins!" said Reuben, resting his steering paddle across the canoe for a few seconds.

Swiftarrow assented with another "Ho," and

Lawrence moved his gun into a handy position to be ready for an emergency; but there was no other sign of man's presence than the wreath of smoke. All was perfectly silent. The air, too, was quite still, and the surface of the lake resembled a sheet of glass.

"Strange," observed Reuben, "redskins ain't usually so shy. If they mean mischief they don't ever let smoke be seen, an' when they don't mean mischief they generally show themselves. Come, push on, lads; we'll go see what's i' the wind."

"I'll show them the muzzle, father," said Lawrence, laying down his paddle and taking up his gun: "it may be well to let 'em see that we have arms."

"No need for that, boy. If they know anything at all, they know that white men don't go about in the wilderness empty-handed. Put down the piece, and use your paddle."

Thus reproved, Lawrence flushed slightly, but obeyed the order and resumed paddling.

In a few minutes they were on shore. Still all was silent as the grave. Hauling the bow of the canoe on the beach to keep it fast, the three men took their weapons, and, entering the woods in single file, walked cautiously but swiftly in the direction of the smoke. They soon reached the spot, and the scene which met their eyes was one which, while it accounted for the silence that reigned around, filled their minds with sadness and horror.

In an open space, where a number of trees had been cut down, stood about a dozen skin tents or Indian lodges, some with the curtain-doors closed, others open, exposing the interiors, on the floors of which the dead bodies of Indian men, women, and children, lay in every attitude and in all stages of decomposition. Outside of the tents other corpses lay strewn on the ground, and most of these bore evidence of having been more or less torn by wolves. The travellers knew at a glance that these unfortunate people had fallen before that terrible disease, smallpox, which had recently attacked and almost depopulated several districts of the Indian country.

How the disease was introduced among the Indians at the time of which we write, it is impossible to say and useless to conjecture. The fact of its desolating effects is unquestionable. One who dwelt in the country at the time writes: [See Sir Alexander Mackenzie's

Voyages, page 14.] "The fatal infection spread around with a baneful rapidity which no flight could escape, and with a fatal effect that nothing could resist. It destroyed with its pestilential breath whole families and tribes; and the horrid scene presented, to those who had the melancholy opportunity of beholding it, a combination of the dead, the dying, and such as, to avoid the fate of their friends around them, prepared to disappoint the plague of its prey by terminating their own existence. To aggravate the picture, if aggravation were possible, the carcases were dragged forth from the huts by the wolves, or were mangled within them by the dogs, which thus sought to satisfy their hunger with the putrid remains of their masters. It was not uncommon at this time for the father of a family, whom the infection had not reached, to call his household around him, represent the terrible sufferings and fate that awaited them, which he believed was owing to the influence of an evil spirit who desired to extirpate the race, and incited them to baffle death with all its horrors by at once killing themselves—at the same time offering to perform the deed of mercy with his own hand if their hearts should fail them."

That some of the dead before our pioneers had acted in this way was evident, for while most of the corpses bore marks of having been smitten with the disease, others were there which showed nothing to account for death save a knife wound over the region of the heart.

It was a sad and sickening sight, and drew forth one or two low-toned sorrowful remarks from Reuben, as he moved slowly towards the tent from which smoke still issued.

The three men paused before it because a sound came from within, and they felt reluctant to disturb the awful silence. The pause, however, was but momentary. Reuben lifted the covering and opened it wide. A small fire still burned on the hearth in the centre of the lodge; around it lay the bodies of dead men, women, and children. Only one figure, that of an old woman, remained in a half-reclining position, but she was motionless, and they thought her dead, also. This, however, was not the case. The flood of light which streamed in on her appeared to rouse her, for she raised her grey head, and, gazing anxiously at the figures which darkened the entrance of the lodge, asked in a tremulous voice: "Is that you, my son?"

"No, mother, but it is a friend," said Swiftarrow, who understood her language.

"A friend," repeated the old woman, shaking her head slowly, "I don't want a friend. The Master of Life is my friend. My people said that an evil spirit was slaying them; but I know better. It was the Great Spirit who came to us. We have been very wicked. We needed punishment. But why has He spared me? I was the worst of them all."

There was something terrible in the tone and manner in which this was uttered, as if the breast of the speaker were torn with conflicting feelings.

"She must have met wi' the missionaries some time or other," whispered Reuben.

"Is the old woman the only one of all the tribe left alive?" asked Swiftarrow.

"Ay, the only one no, not the only one; my son is yet alive. He went to set a bear trap not very long since; but he should have come back before now. He will be back soon."

The deep sigh which followed proved that the poor old woman was hoping against hope.

"How long is't since he left you, Mother?" asked Lawrence eagerly.

"Two suns have risen and set since he left, and he had not far to go."

"Father, I'll go seek for this man," said Lawrence; "something may have befallen him."

Reuben made no objection, and the youth set off immediately in a direction which was pointed out by the old woman.

After he was gone his father and the Indian shifted one of the cleanest looking of the empty tents to a considerable distance from the spot where the terrible work of death had been done, and removing the old woman from the neighbourhood of the pestilential atmosphere, placed her therein, kindled a fire and cooked her a little food, of which she evidently stood much in need.

Meanwhile Lawrence sped through the pathless forest with the light step of a strong youth and the precision of a practised hunter. About four miles from the Indian camp he came upon the track of a bear, the footprints of which proved that it was an unusually large one. He followed it up closely, and was led by it to a spot where some trees had been cut down, and not far from which he saw what appeared to him to be the remains of a trap. Almost at the same moment of his making this discovery he heard a growl, and saw the bear itself a monster of the brown species, which differs from the ordinary black bear of America in being more carnivorous and much larger, as well as more savage and bold. No sooner did it see the youth than it rushed upon him with great fury. A piece of broken line was drawn tight round its neck, and another piece round its fore-leg, while four arrows stuck in its shoulder and side, showing plainly that it had broken loose from a snare and had been attacked by man. But Lawrence had no time to think on these things. He had barely time to throw forward and cock his gun when the bear was upon him. It rose on its hind legs, and in doing so towered high above the youth, who, whatever his feelings might have been, looked undismayed. With an unflinching eye he took aim at the monster's heart, and shot it dead. So close was it to him that he singed the hair on its breast and had to leap to one side to avoid being struck as it fell.

Reloading quickly, the young hunter advanced

towards the trap, where his worst fears were realised, for near to it he found the body of an Indian torn limb from limb, and mostly eaten, except the head, which remained entire. It was evident that the poor man, having set several snares for bears, had gone to visit them, and found this brown bear caught by the head and leg. He seemed to have tried to kill it with arrows, but must have been afraid to go near enough to use his weapons with effect, and the enraged animal, having broken the snare, flew upon him and tore him to pieces.

Brown bears of this kind are very powerful. One traveller in these regions saw the footprints of a large one, which, having seized a moose deer in a river, dragged it for a quarter of a mile along the sandy banks, and afterwards devoured it all except part of the hindquarters; and the moose which had been treated in this unceremonious way, judging from the size and hardness of the bones, must have been upwards of a year old, when it would weigh as much as an ox of the same age.

Collecting the scattered remnants of the unfortunate Indian, who was no other than the old woman's son,

Lawrence covered them over with leaves and sticks. He then skinned the bear and cut off its claws, which he carried away as trophies, along with one or two choice steaks cut from the creature's flank. He also collected the weapons and part of the dress of the Indian, with which he returned to the camp.

"Heyday! Lawrence, what have you got there, lad?" said Reuben, as his son came up and threw the bundle on the ground.

"A brown bear, father."

"Well done!" exclaimed Reuben, with a look of pride, for although his son had shot many a black bear in the forest, he had never before stood face to face with such a monster as that whose skin and claws now lay at his feet.

"It would have been well, father," said Lawrence gravely, "if the man who first saw this had owned a gun. His arrows were no better than needles in such a hide. See here!"

He drew from his breast the bloody portions of dress which had belonged to the slaughtered Indian.

"The son of the old woman has gone to the happy hunting grounds," said Swiftarrow, referring to the heaven of the Indian, as he lifted and examined the dress.

"Ay, ay," said Reuben sadly, "'tis the chances of the wilderness. You'd better tell the poor old creetur', Swiftarrow; you understand her ways and lingo better than me."

Silently the Indian went to the old woman, and laid the bloody garments before her. At first she did not understand what had happened. Suddenly the truth flashed upon her, and she looked quickly up into the grave countenance of the Indian, but death and sorrow appeared to have already done their worst on her, for she neither spoke nor wept for some time. She took up the shreds of cloth and turned them over tenderly; but neither sign nor groan escaped her. Evidently she had been already so stunned by the horrors which had surrounded her for some time, that this additional blow did not tell—at least, not at first—but Reuben observed, while trying to comfort her some time afterwards, that a few tears were coursing slowly down her withered cheeks.

That night, round the campfire, the pioneers held earnest counsel, and resolved, sadly but firmly, that their projected journey must be given up for that season.

"It's a hard thing to do," said Reuben, as he lay at full length before the fire after supper, "to give up our plans after comin' so far; but it ain't possible to carry that old 'ooman along with us an' it's not to be thought of to leave her behind to starve, so there's nothin' for it but to go back an' take her wi' us to the settlements. I would feel like a murderer if I was to leave one o' God's creeturs to perish in the wilderness. What think you, Lawrence?"

"I think you are right, father," replied the youth, with a deep sigh.

"An' what says Swiftarrow?"

"Go back," was the Indian's prompt and laconic answer.

"Well, then, we're all agreed, so we'll turn back on our trail tomorrow; but I shall try again next year if I'm above ground. I once know'd a Yankee who had what he called a motto, an' it was this, `Never give in, 'xcept w'en yer wrong.' I think I'll take to that motto. It seems to me a good 'un."

In proof, we presume, of his sincerity, Reuben Guff

rolled himself in his blanket, stretched his feet towards the fire, pillowed his head on a bundle of moss, and at once gave in to the seductive influences of sleep; an example which was so irresistible that his companions followed it without delay.

Chapter III

INTRODUCES THE KING OF PIONEERS.

Discarding space and ignoring time, we seize you by the hand, reader, and bound away with you still deeper into the northern wilderness, away into that remote region which, at the time we write of, was the ultima thule of the furtraders of Canada,beyond which lay the great unknown world, stretching to the pole. Here, amid the grand scenery of the Rocky Mountains, lies the Athabasca Lake, also styled the Lake of the Hills. We prefer the latter name, as being more romantic.

This is no pretty pond such as we in England are wont to visit and delight in during our summer holidays. It is a great sheet of water; a grand freshwater sea, 200 miles long and 15 miles broad—a fitting gem for the bosom of the mighty region on which it glitters.

A year has fled since the period of our last chapter, and here, in a birchbark canoe on the waters of the Lake of the Hills, we find our pioneers—Reuben Guff, his son Lawrence, and his Indian friend Swiftarrow. There is also a young Indian woman in the canoe—Swiftarrow's wife.

The kind-hearted red man adopted the old woman who had been rescued on their previous trip, but, not finding her a good substitute for his own mother, he bethought him of adding a young squaw to his establishment. While he meditated on this step, the old woman died. About the same time Reuben Guff made proposals to him to join him on a second "v'yage of diskivery." The Indian agreed; got married off-hand, and took his bride along with him. We now find them all four at the Lake of the Hills.

It may be as well to observe, in passing, that Indian brides are usually more robust than those of civilised communities. They are quite competent to follow their lords on the most arduous canoe voyages, and, besides being able to wield the paddle with great dexterity, are exceedingly useful in managing what may be styled the domestic matters of the camp. They also keep up a constant supply of the Indian's indispensable footgear—moccasins—which are so slender in their nature that a pair may be completely worn out in a single day of hard hunting.

The brown bride, therefore, was not a hindrance to the party, but a useful member of it, as well as a pleasant companion. True, her companionship consisted chiefly in answering "yes" and "no" when spoken to, and in smiling pleasantly at all times; but this was sufficient to satisfy the moderate demands of her male friends upon her intellectual resources.

"Fort Chipewyan at last," said Reuben, resting his paddle across the canoe and looking earnestly towards the horizon; "I hope we ain't too late after all our pushin' on. It would be hard to find that Monsieur Mackenzie had started."

"Too much ice in the lake," said Swiftarrow. "He has not gone yet."

"I'm not so sure o' that," observed Lawrence. "If reports be true, Monsieur Mackenzie is not the man to wait until the ice is all off the lakes and nothin' but plain sailin' lies before him."

"That's true, lad," replied Reuben, resuming his paddle. "I wonder," he murmured to himself, as he gazed wistfully towards the unknown north, "I wonder if the big river is really there, an' if it do jine the sea?"

That same question was put to himself that same evening—though not for the first time by one of the inhabitants of Fort Chipewyan. The fort was a mere group of two or three log huts. In the largest of these huts sat a man whose strongly-marked handsome countenance gave evidence of a bold enterprising spirit and a resolute will. He pored over a map for some time, carefully tracing a few pencil lines into the blank spaces on the paper, and then murmured, in words which were almost identical with those of Reuben Guff, "I wonder if it joins the Polar Sea?"

This man was the true pioneer, or, rather, the king of pioneers, to whom Guff gave place without a murmur, for Reuben was a modest man; and the moment he heard that one of the gentlemen of the Canadian fur-trading company had taken up his favourite hobby, and meant to work out the problem, he resolved, as he said, "to play second fiddle," all the more that the man who thus unwittingly supplanted him was a mountaineer of the Scottish Highlands.

"It's of no manner of use, you see," he said to Swiftarrow, when conversing on the subject, "for me to go off on a v'yage o' diskivery w'en a gentleman like Monsieur Mackenzie, with a good edication an' scienteefic knowledge and the wealth of a fur company at his back, is goin' to take it in hand. No; the right thing for Reuben Guff to do in the circumstances is to jine him an' play second fiddle—or third, if need be."

Alexander Mackenzie—while seated in the lowly hut of that solitary outpost poring over his map, trying to penetrate mentally into those mysterious and unknown lands which lay just beyond him— saw, in imagination, a great river winding its course among majestic mountains towards the shores of the ice laden polar seas. He also saw the lofty peaks and snow-clad ridges of that mighty range which forms the backbone of the American continent, and again in imagination—passed beyond it and penetrated the vast wilderness to the Pacific, thus adding new lands to the

British Crown, and opening up new sources of wealth to the fur company of which he was one of the most energetic members. He saw all this in imagination, we say, but he did not, at that time, see his name attached to one of the largest American rivers, classed with the names of the most noted discoverers of the world, and himself knighted. Still less, if possible, did he see, even in his wildest flights of fancy, that the book of travels which he was destined to write, would be translated into French by the order of Napoleon the First, for the express purpose of being studied by Marshal Bernadotte, with the view of enabling that warrior to devise a roundabout and unlooked-for attack on Canada in rear, as it were from the region of the northern wilderness—a fact which is well worthy of record! [See Appendix for an interesting letter on the subject.]

None of these things loomed on the mind of the modest though romantic and enterprising man, for at that time he was only at the beginning of his career of discovery.

It may not be out of place here to say a word or two as to the early career of the hero whose footsteps we are about to follow.

He was a Highlander, to begin with; and possessed all the fire and determination peculiar to that race. At an early period of life he was led to engage in commercial enterprises in the country northwest of Lake Superior, joined the Northwest Fur Company of Canada in 1784, and went into the Indian country the following spring. It is not necessary to say more than that Alexander Mackenzie proved himself to be a first-rate furtrader at a time when the furtrade was carried on under great difficulties and amid severe privations. For many years he was in charge of Fort Chipewyan, the remote establishment to which we have just conducted our reader. Seven years before his coming on the scene, the Lake of the Hills had not been visited by white men, and was known only through Indian report. When Mackenzie became ruler of the district, all beyond the lake was *terra incognita*. His spirit was one which thirsted to explore the unknown. He was eminently fitted both to hold an advanced post and to invade new regions, being robust in constitution, powerful in frame, inquisitive in mind, and enterprising in spirit. Frequently had he arrived at Fort Chipewyan with ninety or a hundred men without any provision for their sustenance for the winter save their fishing nets and guns. He was therefore accustomed to live from hand to mouth, and to depend on his own exertions and resources in a country where the winter is upwards of eight months long and the severity of the climate extreme.

It was in June 1789 that he made preparations to start on his first voyage of discovery.

Rising from the table at which he had been studying his projected route, Mackenzie turned, with the air of a man who has made up his mind, and said to a clerk who was smoking beside the fireplace—

"Le Roux, if we cannot prevail on these Indians to accompany us, I have determined to start without them. Has the small canoe been gummed?"

"It has," answered Le Roux, "but I would advise delay for a day or two. If we give them time, the Indians may change their minds; besides, the ice has not yet sufficiently cleared away."

Mackenzie paced the room impatiently, and his eyes flashed for one moment with impatience. They were deep blue eyes that could beam with melting tenderness or sparkle with suppressed passion—it is but just to add that passion in his case was usually suppressed, for he was a lover of peace, as most truly great and powerful men usually are:

"Let us see now," he said, sitting down in front of Le Roux, "how our resources stand. In my canoe there will be the four Canadians and the German. Then there's our Indian friend, English Chief and his two wives, who will embark in the second-sized canoe. The two young Indians whom we want to accompany us with their wives must make up their minds tonight, else I will start without them. Your own canoe with goods for trade and provisions, will not be fully loaded; I shall therefore place in it the provisions that we can't carry, and when we come to the place where you are to stop and trade, and where I shall bid you farewell, we shall doubtless have eaten our lading down sufficiently to take the whole on board. See, by the way, that the goods and trinkets to be given in presents as we go along are not placed in the wrong canoe."

"They are already laid with the other goods, and also the nets and ammunition by themselves," said Le Roux, rising and laying down his pipe.

At that moment Reuben Guff entered with his friends. The surprise of Mackenzie was great on beholding them, but greater still was his delight when he learned their errand. The young Indians were forthwith told that their services would not now be required, and our friends including Swiftarrow's wife, Darkeye were at once added to the exploring party.

Next day the expedition set forth from Fort Chipewyan and swept over the broad breast of the Lake of the Hills.

We will not trace their course over known ground. Suffice it to say that their troubles began at once. Soon after leaving the lake they came to a rapid part of the river which flows out of it, where they were obliged to land and carry canoes and goods to the still water further down, but here the ice was still unthawed on the banks, rendering the process of reloading difficult. Soon after they came to a place called the Portage d'Embarras, which is occasioned by driftwood filling up the channel of the river. There they entered the Slave River, where there is a portage or carrying-place named the Mountain, the landing at which is very steep and close to the fall. Below this fall there is a mile of dangerous rapids and here they met with their first disaster.

Reuben and Swiftarrow having landed with part of the cargo of the small canoe, had left it in charge of Darkeye, so named because of her large and lustrous eyes, which, however, were the only good points about her, for she was ill-favoured and clumsy, though strong of frame and a diligent worker. While she was moving from one point of rock to another that appeared to her more convenient for landing, the canoe was caught by an eddy and swept in a moment out into the strong current, down which it sped with fearful velocity towards the falls. Darkeye was quite collected and cool, but she happened to dip her paddle on the edge of a sunk rock with such vigour that the canoe overturned. Upon the heights above her husband saw the accident, and stood rooted for a moment in helpless dismay to the spot. It chanced that Lawrence Guff was at the time the only man near the unfortunate woman, who, although she swam like an otter, could not gain the bank. Seeing this, the youth sprang towards a jutting rock that almost overhung the fall, and entering the rushing stream so deeply that he could barely retain his foothold, caught the woman by the hair of the head as she was sweeping towards the edge of the fall. The two swayed for a few seconds on the verge of destruction; then Swiftarrow came bounding down the bank like a deer, and, catching Lawrence by the hand, dragged them both out of danger; but before they were fairly landed the canoe was carried over the falls, dashed to pieces, and in a few seconds its shreds were tossed wildly on the surging rapids far down the river.

This accident caused them little loss beyond the canoe, which was soon replaced by another, purchased from a party of Indians, with whom they fell in that same evening.

Passing through Slave River, they swept out on the bright waters of Great Slave Lake. Over these they sped during several days. This lake is one of the largest freshwater oceans of the continent, about 250 miles long and 50 broad.

And here the work of exploration fairly began. Great Slave Lake was at that time imperfectly known from Indian report; and the river of which they were in search flowed, it was supposed, out of its western extremity. Here also Monsieur Le Roux was to be left behind with a party of men to prosecute the furtrade.

Chapter IV

We have passed over the first three weeks of the voyage rapidly, but it must not be supposed that therefore it was all plain sailing. On the contrary, the travellers were delayed by thunderstorms, and heavy rains, and gales, and impeded by ice, which, even in the middle of June lay thick on the waters in some parts. They were also tormented by hosts of mosquitoes, and at times they found difficulty in procuring food despite the ability of our friends Reuben, Swiftarrow, and Lawrence, who were constituted hunters to the expedition. At other times, however, the supply of food was abundant and varied. On one occasion the hunters brought in seven geese, a beaver, and four ducks, besides which a large supply of excellent trout and other fish was obtained from the nets; and on another occasion they procured two swans, ten beavers, and a goose. But sometimes they returned empty-handed, or with a single bird or so, while the nets produced nothing at all. Deer were also shot occasionally, and they found immense numbers of wild cranberries, strawberries, rasps, and other berries, besides small spring onions; so that, upon the whole, they fared well, and days of abstinence were more than compensated by days of superabundance.

One evening while they were coasting along this great lake, some Indians were discovered on the shore, and the travellers landed to make inquiries of them as to the nature of the country beyond. There were three lodges belonging to the Red-knife Indians, who were so named because their knifes were made of the copper found in that region. To the leading man of these, English Chief, being interpreter, addressed himself.

English Chief, we may remark in passing, was one of the followers of the chief who conducted Hearne on his expedition to the Coppermine River; since which event he had been a principal leader of his countrymen who were in the habit of carrying furs to the English furtraders at Churchill, on Hudson's Bay, and was much attached to the interest of the Hudson Bay Company, which, at that time, was in opposition to the Canadian or Nor'-West Company. These circumstances procured him the title of the English Chief. An able, active, but self-sufficient and somewhat obstinate chief he was, and caused Mackenzie a good deal of anxiety and much trouble to keep him with the party.

In answer to his queries, the principal man of the Red-knife Indians said that there were many more of his tribe a short distance off, and that he would send a man to fetch them. He also said that the explorers should see no more of them at that time, because the Slave and Beaver Indians, as well as others of the tribe, were about to depart, and would not be in that region again till the time when the swans cast their feathers.

"Ask him," said Mackenzie, "if he and his friends have many furs to dispose of."

To this the Indian replied by at once producing

upwards of eight large packs of good beaver and marten skins; and added the information that his friends had plenty more.

"Now, then, Le Roux," said Mackenzie, turning to his clerk, "here you and I shall part. This seems a good spot and a good opportunity for opening up the trade with these Indians. When the rest of them arrive, we shall have a palaver, and then you shall remain to look after them, so, open up your packs, and get ready a few small presents without delay."

That day was spent in considerable bustle and excitement; the Indians being overjoyed that the white traders had at last penetrated into their country; and their joy being increased by the distribution of such trifling, but much-prized, gifts as glass beads, knives, small looking-glasses, etcetera. It rained in torrents all the time, but this did not damped their spirits; and as for their bodies they were used to it! In the afternoon Mackenzie assembled the whole tribe, and made them the following speech, which was translated by English Chief in a very pompous manner, for that excellent redskin was fully alive to the dignity of his position.

"My friends," began our explorer, "I am glad to

meet with you. The white man and the Indians are always glad to meet they can benefit each other mutually. Each has got what the other requires. I have come for the purpose of opening up trade with you. It is true that I myself will take my departure tomorrow, because I am in search of new lands; but some of my people will remain on the spot, and if you bring in a sufficient quantity of furs to make it answer, my men will return to Fort Chipewyan for more goods, and will spend the winter here. They will build a fort and continue to dwell among you as long as you shall be found to deserve it."

At this point the speaker paused, and the dark-skinned audience gave vent to a loud "Ho!" which was equivalent to the British "Hear, hear!"

"In regard to my own work," continued Mackenzie, "I intend to search for, and find the great river, which, it is said, flows out of this lake, and follow its current to the sea or, as you call it, the great salt lake. Do my brothers know anything about this river? If so, let them speak."

Hereupon an old chief, with hair like small iron wire, and a skin like shoe-leather, got up, and delivered himself as follows—

"We are glad to hear what our white brother says. It encourages us to know that you will make a trading fort in our country, for we have need of one. Hitherto we have had to travel far, very far, with our furs; or if, to save trouble, we intrusted our furs to the Chipewyans, they often pillaged us, or, at most, gave us very little for the fruits of our toil. For a long time we have been so discouraged that we had no motive to pursue the beaver, except to obtain a sufficiency of food and clothing. Now if you come to us, we shall be happy wauch!"

The last word was equivalent to the expression "There, think o' that!" The old man paused as if to give his audience time for reflection.

"As to the great river," he continued sententiously, "we know of its existence; but none of our tribe has ever followed its course down to the great salt lake. We earnestly advise our brother not to go there, for it is a dreadful river. It is said that there are two impassable falls in its course; and it is so long that old age will come upon you before the time of your return. You will also encounter monsters of horrid shapes and awful strength on the land and in the water wauch!"

The old chief began to glare solemnly at this point, and the whole tribe followed his example.

"It is said," he continued, "that there are bears which eat the trees as if they were grass; whose cubs, even at their birth, are strong enough to kill the stoutest man. There are monsters in the river so big that a canoe full of men would be but a mouthful to them. There are so few animals or fish fit for food, that you will all certainly be starved. And, besides all this, evil spirits dwell there, whose chief delight lies in attacking, killing, roasting, and devouring men wauch!"

Here the Indian sat down with the decision of a man who has given unanswerable arguments for the overturning of foolish plans; nevertheless, Mackenzie's plans remained unaltered. Not so, however, those of a young Indian, who had been engaged to guide the explorers to the other end of the lake, in order to save them from the loss of time which would be occasioned by the necessity of coasting round its numerous bays. The imagination of this youth Coppernose, as Lawrence Guff facetiously styled him was so wrought upon by the dreadful description of the great river, that he manifested a strong desire to draw back; but by the timely addition of a small kettle, an axe, a knife, and a few beads to the gifts already bestowed on him, he was eventually persuaded to venture.

Before departing, poor Coppernose took a ceremonious leave of his family. He cut off a lock of his hair, and divided it into three parts. One of these he fastened to the top of his wife's head, and blew on it three times with the utmost violence, at the same time uttering certain cabalistic words. The other two portions he fastened with the same formalities to the heads of his two children.

Even at the last he hesitated, and was finally made to enter the canoe more by force than by persuasion!

A few days later, and our pioneers were fairly embarked on the great river, whose course to the mouth it was their object to explore.

The expedition was now somewhat reduced, owing to Monsieur Le Roux having been left behind. It consisted of three canoes—the large one with Mackenzie and five men; a small one, with English Chief and his two wives, and Coppernose; and another small one, containing Reuben, his son, Swiftarrow, and

Darkeye. Two of the Canadians were also attended by their wives; so that the party numbered sixteen souls, five of whom were women. They all kept company as much as possible, but English Chief was frequently left behind by the large canoe; while Reuben and his friends, being the hunters as we have said, were necessarily absent for considerable periods in search of game.

One evening as they were descending a beautiful sweep of the river under sail in grand style, the English Chief leaning composedly back in his canoe, while his right hand slightly moved the steering paddle, and his teeth grasped his beloved pipe said quietly to Coppernose, of course in the Indian tongue—

"A pretty guide you are, not to know something more about a river so near to your own wigwam."

Coppernose, who was a humble-minded man, smiled slightly, and shook his head as he said—

"All red men are not so adventurous as the English Chief. I never had occasion to travel in this direction, and do not know the way."

"Boo!" ejaculated English Chief; meaning, no doubt, fiddlededee!

"But I know of a river," continued Coppernose, "which falls into this one from the north, and comes from the Horn Mountain that we passed at the end of Great Slave Lake; it is the country of the Beaver Indians. My relations meet me frequently on that river. There are great plains on both sides of that river, which abound in buffaloes and moose deer."

"I don't believe it wauch!" said English Chief. As this was a discouraging reception of his remarks, Coppernose relapsed into silence.

Soon afterwards the large canoe was observed to make for a low grassy point; and as it was about the usual camping time, English Chief made for the same place. The hunters reached it about ten minutes later, and bore into camp two reindeer, four geese, and a swan, besides a large quantity of berries gathered by the fair (or brown) hands of Darkeye.

"There is plenty of game everywhere," said Reuben, in answer to a query from his leader, "we might have killed much more if we'd had more time but enough is as good as a feast, as the sayin' goes in my country."

"In your country?" said Mackenzie, with a smile.

"Ay, I claim to be a Scotchman though I was born

and raised in Canada my father hailed from the land o' cakes."

"Does Lawrence claim the same nationality on the same ground, Reuben?"

"He does not!" answered Lawrence for himself, while busy cleaning his father's gun.

"The lad loves the Canadians," replied Reuben, with a chuckle; "besides, he couldn't claim it on the same ground, seein' that I am fully half a Scot, while he is at least three-quarters a Canadian."

"More the better luck for him," said one of the Canadians, who had already kindled a fire, before which one of his comrades was busily engaged setting up juicy venison steaks to roast.

"Oui," observed another; "vraiment, Canada beats Scottish land altogeder."

"Ha! Faderland ees more best, den all ze vorld," said the German, quaffing a can of water with as much zest as if it had been his own native Rhine wine.

"I warrant me," said Mackenzie with a laugh, "that our trusty guide, Coppernose, would not give the wilderness here for Canada, Scotland, and Faderland put together. What say you, lad?"

Coppernose looked gravely at his questioner, but made no reply.

"Boo!" said English Chief; regarding his countryman with a look of contempt; "hims no onerstan' Eengleesh."

"He understands how to eat a rumpsteak of venison, however," said Mackenzie, with a laugh, as Coppernose at that moment coolly appropriated a mass of half-roasted meat, and began to devour it. "You'd better follow his example, lads."

The men were not slow to take this advice. In a short time all were more or less busily engaged with venison steaks, marrowbones, goose drumsticks, and fish; and comparative silence prevailed while the cravings of nature were being appeased. After supper, pipes were lighted, and conversation became animated for some time; but they were all too much fatigued to prolong this period, interesting though it was. One after another they spread their blankets under a convenient bush or tree, and, ere long, the whole party was in the land of Nod.

Chapter V

DESCRIBES A LITERAL WILD-GOOSE
CHASE AND OTHER MATTERS.

Time sped on its proverbially rapid wing; the summer advanced, and still Mackenzie and his men continued to descend the mighty river of the far north, encountering dangers and vicissitudes enough undoubtedly, but happily escaping those terrified monsters of the forest and the flood, which had been described by the Copper Indians of Great Slave Lake, and the thought of which caused poor Coppernose himself to grow terrified and desperate by turns. Fain would that unhappy son of the forest have bid the party farewell, and returned to his own wigwam alone;

but this might not be, for his services were of some importance, and the leader of the expedition kept on him constantly an eye, which excelled in intense watchfulness the glare of the fiercest of those creatures which filled his imagination. He submitted, therefore, with the best grace he could assume; but, what between being watched by Mackenzie, haunted by ghosts, and bullied by English Chief, poor Coppernose had a sad time of it. He possessed, however, a naturally elastic and jovial spirit, which tended greatly to ameliorate his condition; and as time passed by without any serious mishap, or the appearance of any unusually dreadful creature, he became gradually reconciled to his position.

One day perhaps we should rather say one night, for it was approaching midnight, although the sun was still above the horizon, owing to the high northern latitude to which they had attained, rendering the whole twenty-four hours round a continuous day one day (or night) as the canoes were sweeping down a reach of the broad river, they saw a few wreaths of smoke rising above the treetops. The spot was very beautiful, being thickly wooded and backed by high land, on the slopes of which the trees and bushes hung like delicate fringes of green among masses of silvery grey rock.

"That looks like the smoke of an Indian wigwam, Louis," said Mackenzie to his bowman.

"No, monsieur, it is the wood burning," replied Louis, dipping his vermilion-painted paddle with great vigour.

Louis was right, for soon afterwards they turned a point which disclosed to their view a considerable tract of woodland which had been recently destroyed by fire. Several tracts of this kind had been already passed, some of which had been consumed long before, and forests of young poplars had grown up in their places a curious circumstance this, which Mackenzie remarks on, namely, "That wherever land covered with spruce, pine, and white birch had been laid waste with fire, there poplars, and nothing else, were found to grow, even though none of that species of tree had existed there before."

Passing this desolated tract, they came to a part of the river which was studded with several islands, on one of which reindeer were seen.

"There's your chance," said Mackenzie to his hunters, who happened to range up alongside in their small canoe at that moment.

"We've seed 'em, monsieur," said Reuben, "but we must have some more ammunition afore startin' after them, for the powderhorns of Lawrence and Swiftarrow are both empty."

As soon as the horns were replenished, Reuben and his friends pushed out into the stream and made for the island. The other canoes continued to advance. They seldom waited for the hunters, for the latter being comparatively light, could act as a sort of flying artillery, falling behind, turning aside, or pushing ahead, as the case might require, in pursuit of game, and almost always returning to the main body about the camping hour, or soon after it. On this evening, however, the canoes reached a snug campground before the usual time; they therefore determined to stop there and set the nets, as well as to overhaul the canoes, which stood much in need of repair. The cold of the ice laden waters, through which they had recently passed, had cracked the gum off the seams, and collisions with the ice itself had made some ugly slits in the birchbark of which the canoes were made.

That evening the nets, which were set in four fathoms water, produced an abundant supply of carp, whitefish, and trout.

"Now, lads," said Mackenzie, when the canoe brought ashore the welcome provisions, "set the women to work to make pemmican, for we must leave a supply concealed here against our return."

Louis Blanc superintended the making of this pemmican, which consisted of fish dried in the sun and pounded between two stones. Pemmican is also made of meat, in which case the pounded meat is put into a bag made of the raw hide of the animal; the bag is then filled with melted fat and the mouth sewed up with raw sinews. This style of pemmican will keep fresh for years.

"Where did English Chief go when we landed?" asked Mackenzie.

"Don't know, monsieur," replied Louis.

"After game, probably," observed the leader, as he sat down on the stump of a fallen tree and began to make notes in his journal.

Some time thereafter, Reuben's canoe returned

laden with two deer, besides two swans, a number of ducks and hares, and several brace of ptarmigan, which latter were quite grey at that season, with the exception of one or two pure white feathers in the tail. They said that wild fowl were innumerable among the islands; but this, indeed, was obvious to all, for everywhere their plaintive and peculiar cries, and the whirring or flapping of their wings, were heard even when the leafy screen over the encampment hid themselves from view. Darkeye also contributed her share to the general supplies, in the shape of several large birch-baskets full of gooseberries, cranberries, juniper berries, rasps, and other wild berries, which, she said, grew luxuriantly in many places.

Meanwhile, the night (as regards time) advanced, although the daylight did not disappear, or even much diminish, but English Chief, with Coppernose and his two squaws, did not return, and their prolonged absence became at length a cause of no little anxiety to the leader of the expedition. The fact was that English Chief was fond of a little fun, and despite the dignified position which he held, and the maturity of his years, he could not resist availing himself of any little chance that came in his way of having what is more pithily than elegantly styled "a spree."

It happened to be the particular period at which the wild fowl of those regions begin to cast their feathers. Knowing this, English Chief quietly slipped off with his canoe when Mackenzie landed, and soon found a colony of swans afflicted with that humiliating lack of natural clothing, which is the cause, doubtless, of their periodically betaking themselves to the uttermost ends of the earth in order to hide in deep solitude their poverty, and there renew their garments. Judge then, reader, if you can, the consternation with which these once graceful creatures discovered that their retreat had been found out by that inquisitive biped, man that they were actually caught in the act of moulting!

Uttering a terrific "hoozoo!" or some such equally wild Red Indian hunting cry, English Chief dashed his paddle into the water; squaws and comrade followed suit; the canoe shot in among the rushes, and the whole party leaped on shore. Thus taken by surprise the swans bounced up, extended their miserable wings, uttered a trumpet blast of alarm, and sought to fly. Of course they failed, but although they could not fly, they fled on the wings of terror, and with straight necks, heads low, legs doing double duty, and remnants of wings doing what they could, they made for the interior of the island at a pace which at first defied pursuit.

The higher part of the island was level and open, with here and there a few stunted bushes.

Arrived here the trumpeting crew scattered, like wise troops when pursued. English Chief set his heart and eyes on a particularly large bird, and dashed after it with upraised paddle. The swan made a desperate detour, apparently bent on gaining the water; it ran round a bush, and was almost caught in the arms of the younger squaw, who, leaving her senior in the canoe, had joined in the pursuit. A shriek from the squaw sent it off at a tangent to the left, pinions aloft, and terror depicted on its visage. English Chief also doubled, but a crooked stump caught his foot and sent him headlong into the bush. At that instant, Coppernose, having foiled a swan with a well-directed sweep of his paddle, came up and gave chase. English Chief, nettled at the interference, sprung up, followed and overtook him just as the hard-pushed swan turned at bay. Both men came upon it at the same moment, stumbled over it, and turned their wrath upon each other. The swan, recovering, ran wildly and blindly back towards the young squaw, who was so much alarmed by its look that she fairly turned and fled; but hearing the shouts of the Indians as they struggled, she turned towards them. Meanwhile, the elder squaw having landed, met the retreating swan just as it gained the rushes. Stooping down she allowed it to approach to within a yard of her like a true heroine and then, rising, hit it a neat blow on the back of the head and laid it low for ever.

After this she joined her sister-wife (if we may be allowed the expression) in trying to tear the Indians asunder. This was accomplished after a few seconds, but the two men still glared at each other. Fortunately, they could do little more, having left their knives in the canoe. While they were still in a state of indecision, an unfortunate swan, which had taken refuge behind a bush, so far recovered its breath as to think it advisable to get still further away from such company. It was observed and followed as wildly as before by English Chief. This time Coppernose had the sense to confine his attentions to another part of the field, where, while prosecuting the chase, he suddenly came upon a flock of geese in the same helpless circumstances as the swans. Soon the swans were routed out of their places of concealment, and the cries of men, women, and birds again resounded in the air. The way in which those swans behaved was quite marvellous. They dodged the blows aimed at them, and "jinked" round the bushes as if they had been trained to such work in a regular public school for human bipeds, and they struck out with their pinions, too, so deftly and with such force that the pursuers had to become extremely cautious as well as bold in their approaches.

At last, when the Indians were thoroughly exhausted, they gave up the chase. On conveying the fruits of their exertions to the canoe, they found that they had killed five swans and a like number of geese. With these they returned in triumph to camp, to the great relief of Mackenzie, who had begun to fear either that an accident had befallen them, or that they had deserted him.

At this place two bags of pemmican were concealed on an island, and here one of their leads was lost in taking soundings. The current of the river also was so violent that Mackenzie concluded they must be approaching the rapids, of which some of the natives had made mention. The strength of the current may be estimated from the fact that, when the lead just referred to caught on the bottom and held on, they attempted to clear it by paddling up stream; yet although they had eight paddles, and were held by the line, the strength of which was equal to four paddles, they were borne down with such force that the line snapped asunder.

Here the weather became very bad. They had frequent thunderstorms accompanied with violent rain, and, although it was at that time the beginning of July, ice lay in great quantities all along the banks of the river. On shore, the earth was thawed only to a depth of about fourteen inches. Indeed, the soil of those regions never thaws completely. At the hottest season of the year, if you were to dig down a few feet, you would come to a subsoil which is locked in the embrace of perpetual frost. Some signs of natives were discovered here, and, from the appearance of the cut trees, it was evident that they possessed no iron tools.

"Push forward," was Mackenzie's watchword more

perhaps than it had been of any previous discoverer in Rupert's Land. The Indians began ere long to complain bitterly of his perseverance. They were not accustomed to such constant and severe exertion, and it was with great difficulty that he prevailed on them to continue the voyage.

As they advanced, fresh signs of natives were observed, and at last, one evening, they came in sight of an encampment of them. It was at a place where the current of the great river was so strong that it was in actual ebullition, and produced a hissing noise like a kettle of water in a moderate boiling state. The region was mountainous, and just before them they perceived a high ridge covered with snow.

"They're evidently not much used to visitors," said Mackenzie, on observing that the natives were running about in great confusion, some making for the woods, and others hurrying to the canoes.

"They is used to be 'tacked by inimis," said English Chief, who was rather proud of his knowledge of the English language.

"Hail them in the Chipewyan tongue," said Mackenzie, as the canoes touched the beach. English

Chief and the hunters landed first, and addressed the few natives who had ventured to remain, but they were so terrified as to be unable to reply. Seeing this, Mackenzie quietly landed, and gave orders for the pitching of the tents. While this was being done, the natives grew calm; they found that they understood Chipewyan; a few words relieved them of their apprehensions, and soon they not only came down to the tents, but were so gratified with their reception that they sent for those members of their tribe who had fled. Thus, friendly relations were established.

There were five families, consisting of about thirty persons of two different tribes the Slave and the Dog-rib Indians.

Chapter VI

Heroes are not perfect'. We deem it necessary to make this observation, because many modern biographers seem to imagine that their heroes are perfect, and even attempt to prove them to be so. We, therefore, feel it necessary to disclaim any such imagination or intention in regard to our hero. Alexander Mackenzie was indeed a hero, and a very fine specimen of a man mentally as well as physically if we are to credit the report of those who knew him best; but he was not perfect.

For instance, he evidently acted sometimes on

the fallacious notion that whatever gave pleasure to himself must necessarily give pleasure to all other men. Acting on this idea in the present instance, he sought to delight the hearts of these Slave and Dog-rib Indians by presenting them with pipes and tobacco, and inducing them to smoke. To the credit of humanity be it recorded that they received the gift with marked dislike, although they were too polite to absolutely refuse it. Slaves though one section of them were in name, they were not slaves to tobacco; and the other section being Dog-ribs, had, we presume, too little of Adam's rib in them to find pleasure in smoke. Of course, they knew something about smoke, but it was chiefly as a nuisance, which was very troublesome to the eyes, and which usually issued from the tops of their wigwams not from human lips. It must also be recorded that those estimable savages entertained a strong antipathy to grog when it was produced. Their hearts were reached, however, and their souls gladdened, when knives, beads, awls, firesteels, flints, and hatchets were presented to them; and we can fancy how animated and earnest would be their conversation over the wigwam fires, for weeks and months, if not for years, afterwards, when they brought out, for the thousandth time, and feasted their wondering eyes on, those delightfully useful implements, which had been left by the mysterious white beings who had dropped upon them so suddenly, as if from the skies, and whom they felt half inclined at first to reverence as gods.

Having won their confidence and esteem, Mackenzie proceeded to question them as to that portion of the great river which yet lay before him. Their account was an exaggerated echo of that previously obtained from the Indians of Great Slave Lake. Being, therefore, of little or no value, our hero was obliged to advance, and solve the question for himself. As before, the effect of the Indian stories on the Indians of his party was very marked and discouraging. With great difficulty Mackenzie overcame their objections to proceed, and even succeeded in persuading one of the Dog-rib Indians to accompany him by the potent influence of a small kettle, an axe, a knife, and a few other gifts. This man was a stout young fellow, in a very dirty deerskin coat and leggings, with a double blue line tattooed on his cheeks from the ears to the nose, on the bridge of which it met in a blue spot. Hence Lawrence, following the natural bent of his mind, which he had already displayed in naming Coppernose, immediately addressed this new recruit as Bluenose.

These poor savages, although exemplary in the matters of grog and tobacco, were, we are constrained to admit, a very filthy set of creatures; very poor also, because utterly destitute of such wealth as the furtraders had carried to many of the less remote tribes of Indians. Nevertheless, they possessed a considerable number of implements of their own manufacture, some of wood and others of bone, etcetera, which proved them to be possessed of much ingenuity and taste. The description of their weapons reminds one of those remains of prehistoric man which we find treasured in our museums, for they had arrows barbed with horn, flint, iron, and copper, spears shod with bone, daggers of horn and bone, and axes made of brown or grey stone. The latter were from six to eight inches long and two thick, having the inside flat and the outside round, and tapering to an edge, and were fastened by the middle to wooden handles with a cord of raw skin. They kindled fires by striking together a piece of white or yellow pyrites and a flint stone over a piece of touchwood, and boiled water in watertight baskets, by putting a succession of red-hot stones into them.

From these Indians the explorers learned that they had passed, on their voyage down the river, large bodies of Indians who inhabit the mountains.

"He'll never make up his mind to go," observed Reuben, as, when about to set forth again, he looked at the pale countenance of the Dog-rib who had agreed to join the party.

Mackenzie had already had a severe argument with him in order to induce him to fulfil his engagement, and had left him under the impression that he had been successful; but when the poor man had said farewell to the tribe, and was on the point of entering the canoe, his courage failed, and he drew back. Seeing this, Lawrence suddenly seized him by the nape of the neck, and exclaiming, "Come, look sharp, Bluenose, get in with 'ee," gave him a lift that put the matter at rest by sending him sprawling on board. Next moment they were off, and shooting down the rapid current of the river.

That night they encamped, amid heavy squalls of

wind and rain, at the foot of a rocky hill, on the top of which their new guide said that it blew a gale every day of the year! Here the Dog-rib became very unhappy, and pretended to be ill, but a strict watch was kept on him so that he could not escape. The country around them was very wild and rugged, and they were informed by their guide that great numbers of bears and small white buffaloes (muskoxen?) frequented the mountains; also some tribes of Indians. Here some of the party attempted to ascend a steep hill, but were almost suffocated and fairly driven back by clouds of mosquitoes.

Natives were sometimes seen and spoken with, although their first impulse on beholding the voyagers was almost invariably to flee. On one occasion a whole tribe fled save one old man, who came boldly forward and said that he was too old to run or to care much about the short time that yet remained to him of this life. At the same time he pulled out his grey hair by handfuls, and distributed them among the party, imploring their favour for himself and his relations. His mind was quickly relieved by Swiftarrow, who seemed to have a special desire, as well as talent, for comforting aged persons of both sexes.

Some of these tribes were named the Hare Indians hares and fish being their principal means of support. While spending a night with these people a storm of thunder and rain came on, in the midst of which the Dog-rib, Bluenose, managed to make his escape. As it was important to have a guide, Mackenzie compelled a Hare Indian to fill his place; and, after carrying him off, took great pains to conciliate him in which efforts he was happily successful.

Next day they observed natives on the east shore of the river, and directed their course towards them. Their new guide began to call to them in an incomprehensible manner, and said that the natives did not belong to his tribe, but were a very wicked people, who would beat them cruelly, and pull out their hair, and maltreat them in various ways. Despite this warning Mackenzie advanced, and soon found them to be quite as willing to accept gifts as other tribes. He found that they understood their guide, and that English Chief clearly comprehended one of themselves, although he could not make himself understood. Here the joyful information was obtained that in three days more they should meet with the Esquimaux, and in ten days at furthest reach the great salt lake or the sea.

These natives were very superior to those whom the travellers had last met with, and one of them was engaged to take the place of Bluenose. This man, who was clad in a shirt made of the skins of the muskrat, after which he was named, was a very lively individual. He sang the songs not only of his own tribe, but also those of the Esquimaux, with whom his tribe had been formerly at war, but were now at peace. He also undertook to perform an Esquimaux dance in Mackenzie's canoe, and would infallibly have upset that conveyance had he not been violently restrained. He commented on the tribe to which Bluenose belonged with great contempt, calling them by the strong names of cowards and liars.

During these brief visits to the natives, our discoverer was not only troubled by the thievish propensities of the natives, but had to guard against the same tendencies in his own men, some of whom were much confused as to the true course of rectitude in regard to "mine and thine"; in addition to which he had to contend with a general propensity on the part of his men to quarrel not only with each other, but with the weather, the journey, and the decrees of fate generally. By a judicious mixture, however, of firmness and suavity, severity and kindness, he managed to keep the several parts of his discordant band together; and, in so doing, proved himself an able general for the highest generalship consists in making the most of existing circumstances and materials.

The river here ran through various channels formed by islands, some of which were without a tree, while others were covered with spruce, fir, and other trees. The banks, which were about six feet above the surface of the river, displayed a face of solid ice intermixed with veins of black earth, and as the heat of the sun melted the ice, the trees frequently fell into the river. The variety of channels in the river rendered it difficult to decide which should be followed. Muskrat, the new guide, recommended that which ran to the east; but his leader, not feeling sure of his wisdom or knowledge, preferred the middle channel.

Here Mackenzie put ashore and proceeded to engage in some cabalistic pursuits which utterly confounded Muskrat.

"What is he doing?" asked the savage of English Chief.

"Taking the sun," replied the interpreter, with immense pomposity.

"What does that mean?" asked the savage.

English Chief tried to explain, but failed for this good reason that he himself was totally ignorant of the subject beyond the phrase, which he had picked up after the manner of a parrot.

It was found that the latitude was 67 degrees 47 minutes north. This was further north than Mackenzie had expected to make it, but the difference was owing to the variation of the compass. From this it became evident that the river emptied itself into the Polar Sea. Not satisfied, however, with the apparent certainty of this, our pioneer resolved to have ocular demonstration to push on to the mouth of the river, even although, by so doing, he should risk not being able to return to Fort Chipewyan for want of provisions.

But now his men became so much discouraged that they did their utmost to induce him to turn back, and he felt convinced that if they had had it in their power, some of them would have left him to his fate. As Columbus did of old, in somewhat similar circumstances, he assured them that he would now advance only a specified number of days—seven, adding that if he did not then reach the sea he would return. Indeed the low state of their provisions alone formed a sufficient security for the maintenance of his engagement.

That evening (the 11th July) they pitched their tents near to a spot where there had been three encampments of the Esquimaux, and here Mackenzie sat up all night to observe the sun, being now in that realm of bright unchanging day, which in winter becomes a region of continuous night.

At half-past twelve he called up Reuben Guff and his son and Swiftarrow, who were the most intelligent members of his party, to view a spectacle which they had never before seen. They thought, on observing the sun so high, that it was the signal to embark, and were about to rouse their comrades, when Mackenzie checked them, and it was with difficulty he persuaded them that the sun had not descended nearer to the horizon, and that it was then but a short time past midnight!

It is but justice to Reuben and his party to say that they offered no opposition to their leader during the whole voyage. In regard to this, one speech made by Reuben will suffice to describe the spirit that animated him.

"It don't do, Lawrence," said he, "to go for to interfere wi' them as leads. Be they wise or be they foolish it on'y makes matters wus to interfere wi' leaders, my lad; therefore, it's best always to hold your tongue an' do yer dooty. What Monsieur Mackenzie is, it ain't for the likes of you and me to pretend for to judge. He seems to me an able, brave, and wise man, so my colours is nailed to the mast, d'ye see—as was said by the immortal Lord Nelson an' I've made up my mind to follow him to the end, through thick and thin. It's little right I would have to claim to be a pioneer if I didn't hold them sentiments."

"Them sentiments," we need scarcely add, were heartily echoed by his Indian friend and his son.

The appearance of deserted native encampments still further confirmed Mackenzie in his belief that he had at length reached the land of the Esquimaux.

Around their fireplaces were found scattered pieces of whalebone, and spots were observed where train oil had been spilt. The deserted huts also corresponded in construction with those which were known to be built elsewhere by the denizens of the far north. Several runners of sledges were also found, and the skulls of a large animal, which was conjectured to be the walrus. Here the land was covered with short grass and flowers, though the earth was not thawed above four inches from the surface; beneath that all was frozen hard.

The pioneers had now at last reached the entrance of what appeared to be a lake, which was in the neighbourhood of the Polar Sea, if not that sea itself; but the variety of channels, the strength of currents, the shallowness of the water and quantity of ice with which it was beset, with the ignorance of their guide, rendered it impossible to make any further advance that season. The object of the expedition, however, had been accomplished. The largest northern river of America, estimated at 2000 miles in length, had been traced from its source to its outlet in the Polar Sea; the nature of the country and its inhabitants had been ascertained; coal and copper ore had been discovered; the region had been wrenched from the realms of *terra incognita,* and the energetic pioneer fixed the position of his most northerly discoveries in 69 degrees 7 minutes north latitude. Another fact which proved that they were within the influence of the sea was the rise and fall of the water, which could be nothing else than the tide.

They caught a fish, also, resembling a herring, which none of the party had ever seen except English Chief who declared it to be of a kind that abounds in Hudson's Bay, and finally they beheld what settled the question, a shoal of white whales, which their Indian guide said was the principal food of the Esquimaux.

It was no wonder that the discoverers found the navigation very intricate, because that great river, now named the Mackenzie, is known to empty its waters into the Polar Sea by innumerable mouths which form a delta of about forty miles in width. Storms, rain, and fogs, threw additional hindrances in their way. There was, therefore, nothing left for it but to erect a post and take possession of the land in the name of the King.

After that, homeward was the order of the day. But

what a mighty distance off that home was! And, after all, when reached it was but a log hut or two in a part of the vast wilderness which, regarded from a civilised land point of view, was itself the very confines of the known world. Our space forbids us to follow Mackenzie and his men on their arduous and interesting return voyage. Suffice it to say that they dragged the canoes by means of lines against the strong current for a large portion of the way; and, after incurring innumerable dangers from natives, rapids, storms, and starvation, they reached the Lake of the Hills and landed at Fort Chipewyan on the 12th of September 1789, having been absent for the long period of one hundred and two days.

That our hero was not content to rest upon the laurels thus gathered in the far north, but longed to act the part of pioneer over the Rocky Mountains into the far west, shall be made plain in our next chapter.

Chapter VII

A VOYAGE OF DISCOVERY TO THE FAR
WEST PLANNED AND BEGUN.

Three years passed away, during which period Mackenzie, being busily occupied with his arduous duties as a furtrader, could not carry out the more noble purposes of discovery on which his heart was set. But a time at length arrived when circumstances permitted him to turn his eyes once more with a set purpose on the unknown wilderness of the West. Seated one fine morning about the beginning of spring, in his wooden residence at Fort Chipewyan, he observed Reuben Guff passing the window with an axe on his shoulder, that worthy, with his son and Swiftarrow, having engaged in the service of the furtraders at the end of the late expedition. Opening the door, Mackenzie called him in.

"Where are you bound for just now, Reuben?"

"To dinner, monsieur."

"Reuben," said Mackenzie, with a peculiar look, "has all your pioneering enthusiasm oozed out at your finger ends?"

"No, monsieur," replied the man, with a slight smile, "but Lawrence and I have bin thinkin' of late that as Monsieur Mackenzie seems to have lost heart, we must undertake a v'yage o' diskivery on our own account!"

"Good. Then you are both ready, doubtless, to begin your discoveries with a canoe journey of some extent on short notice?"

"At once, monsieur, if it please you."

"Nay, Reuben, not quite so fast as that," said Mackenzie, with a laugh; "you may have your dinner first. But tomorrow you shall become a genuine pioneer by preceding me towards the far west. You know the position of our most distant settlements on the Peace River?"

"Perfectly," said Reuben, whose eye kindled as he

began to see that his master was in earnest.

"Well, I intend to visit these settlements this fall, and push on towards the Rocky Mountains. It will take me to the end of the season to accomplish this, so that our real voyage of discovery will not begin until the following spring. Now, there is a certain locality beyond our most distant outpost, which I shall describe to you afterwards, where I intend to build a fort and spend next winter, so as to be on the spot ready to begin the moment the ice breaks up. Preparations must be made there for the building of the fort. Timber must be felled, cut, and squared for the houses and palisades, and two able and willing, as well as experienced men, must go there to begin this work without delay. It occurs to me that the two best men I have for such work are Reuben Guff and his son. Are they prepared for this duty, think you?"

"Say the word, monsieur," was Reuben's laconic but significant reply.

"Well, then, it is said. Come back here after dinner with Lawrence, and I will give you instructions: you shall start tomorrow at daybreak."

Reuben bowed and left the hall with a light step.

Next day he and his son started on their journey in a small birchbark canoe; on the 10th of October Mackenzie followed in a canoe of larger dimensions. He visited several establishments of the district of which he had charge; ascended the Peace River towards its unknown sources, gave good advice to the several bands of Indians whom he met with by the way, and generally strengthened the hearts and hands of his agents. Passing the last outpost on the river, he pushed on, until, finally, he reached his intended winter-quarters on the 1st of November not a day too soon, for the river was already being covered with its winter coat of ice.

Here he found Reuben and Lawrence, bronzed and hardened with toil and exposure. They had done good service during the previous summer, for all the timber was prepared, a space marked out for the fort, and a deep trench dug for the palisades. Here also were found a band of natives, amounting to about seventy men, anxiously awaiting the arrival of the Chief, as they styled Mackenzie, and thirsting especially for tobacco and rum, both of which unlike the natives of the far north—they were particularly fond of.

To build a fort in a few weeks, consisting of a dwelling-house and several stores, with palisades eighteen feet high, in the midst of frost so intense that their axes sometimes became as brittle as glass, and living in tents the while, exposed to the storms of wind and snow peculiar to a hyperborean clime, was a feat which, if detailed, would fill a volume. We are constrained to dismiss the subject in a line. Thus curtly, also, must we treat the winter. Yet some points we cannot forbear to touch on, illustrative as they are of some curious experiences of the furtraders.

The Indians there were unusually ignorant of medical science, and when ill applied to Mackenzie, believing, with childlike simplicity, that he certainly knew everything and could do anything!

One time an Indian, while at work in the woods was attacked with a sudden pain near the first joint of his thumb, which disabled him. He appealed to Mackenzie, who, to his surprise, found a narrow red inflamed stripe about an inch wide, extending from the man's thumb to his shoulder. The pain was very violent, and accompanied with chilliness and shivering. Mackenzie admits that the case was quite beyond his skill; but as it was necessary to relieve the Indian's mind, he attempted a cure. He prepared a kind of volatile liniment of rum and soap, with which he ordered the arm to be rubbed. The success of this treatment was doubtful, because at first it drove the man mad, and the red stripe not only increased but extended in the form of several blotches on the body, and was accompanied by pains in the stomach. Seeing this, our amateur doctor fell back on the old plan of bleeding, an operation which he had never before performed. The result was marvellous. The following night the man was much better, and ere long was restored to his former health, and filled with gratitude.

Again, on another occasion, a young Indian's gun burst and maimed his hand so that the thumb hung by a mere strip of flesh. When he came to the fort his wound was in a very offensive state. His friends had done their best for him, but as their panacea for everything consisted in singing or howling, and blowing on the affected part, he was not perceptibly the better for their exertions. The youth's life being in danger, Mackenzie once more tried his skill. He applied to it a poultice of bark stripped from the roots of the spruce fir, having first washed the wound with the juice of the bark. This proved to be a very painful dressing, but it cleaned the wound effectually. He then cut off the pendent thumb, and applied a dressing of salve composed of Canadian balsam, wax, and tallow dropped from a burning candle into the water. As before, the treatment was successful, insomuch that the young redskin was soon in the hunting-field again, and brought an elk's tongue as a fee to his benefactor.

During the winter he was visited by a few Rocky Mountain Indians, who gave him some important information; namely, that the Peace River in the mountain districts was interrupted by numerous bad rapids and falls, and that, towards the midday sun, there was another great river whose current ran in an opposite direction, the distance between the sources of the two rivers being short.

The winter, with its dreary storms and bitter colds, at length passed away, and genial spring returned. As soon as the ice broke up, preparations were made for an immediate start. Their large birchbark canoe had been overhauled and repaired. Her dimensions were twenty-five feet long inside, two feet two inches deep, and four feet nine inches wide. She carried goods for presents, provisions, arms, ammunition, baggage, etcetera, to the extent of three thousand pounds weight, with a crew of ten men, including their chief; yet she was so light that two men could carry her when empty for three or four miles without resting. They had no small canoe on this voyage. Their hopes, and, it may be truly said, their lives, were dependent on this solitary and frail conveyance.

As we have said, Mackenzie took nine men with him on this occasion, our friends Reuben, Lawrence, and Swiftarrow being among the number, and two of them being young Indian hunters of that region, who were supposed to be acquainted with at least part of the route they were about to pursue, and who were to act as interpreters. English Chief had long before left his former master, and no women were allowed to go with the party even Darkeye was left behind! There was one other member of the party whom we must not omit to mention namely, a large dog named Wolf.

On the 9th of May 1793, Mackenzie left the fort in charge of his interpreter, pushed off into the waters of the Peace River, turned the canoe's bow westward, and the voyage of discovery began.

A few days afterwards they passed through scenery which all confessed was the most beautiful they had ever beheld.

"'Tis like a glimpse o' paradise," exclaimed Reuben, as the whole party rested on their paddles for a few minutes to gaze upon it.

"Ho!" exclaimed Swiftarrow, with a nod to his friend, which evidently was meant for assent.

"Betterer nor the Hudson," said Ducette, one of the Canadians, with a look of admiration.

"Does it beat Scottisland, monsieur?" asked Lawrence, with a somewhat sly expression.

"Well, ahem," replied Mackenzie with hesitation, "it's not exactly—that is, it is vastly different and truly magnificent—they won't compare, Lawrence; they won't compare!"

The region did indeed merit all that could be said in its praise. The ground on the west side of the river which was wide and full of lovely wooded islets rose at intervals to a considerable height, and stretched inwards to a great distance; at the foot of every slope there was a soft, grassy lawn, broken here and there by abrupt precipices, which were fringed with exuberant verdure. Shrubs and trees of every kind, in clumps and in groves, crested the heights or nestled in the hollows: among them were groves of poplar, with the white spruce and soft birch, and other trees; while the banks abounded with alders and willows. Those that bore blossom were just opening their bright buds, and the setting sun cast a rich golden light over all, as though the glory of the beneficent Creator were shining on His gorgeous handiwork. But that beautiful wilderness did not blossom and bloom in solitude. It was tenanted and enjoyed by countless numbers of living creatures. Wherever the travellers turned their eyes, vast herds of elk and buffaloes were to be seen, the latter sporting with their young ones on the plains, the former preferring to browse on the slopes and uplands; and innumerable birds of all shapes and sizes enlivened the scene with their varied gyrations, and filled the air with melody.

It seemed, indeed, a species of paradise; but not far from it the travellers were painfully reminded of its terrestrial nature by the sight of a widespread conflagration, which carried fierce destruction over the whole plain, and left black ruin behind; and still further on Mackenzie was robbed of the pleasurable feelings due to the influence of sweet scenery, by the baleful influence of man in the shape of a chief of the Beaver Indians with a hunting party. He tried to push on past these Indians, but they kept up with the canoe, running along shore, and when night approached he was compelled to encamp with them. The consequence was, as he had feared, that these people attempted to terrify his young Indian interpreters with dreadful accounts of the land beyond, and succeeded so far that it was with the utmost difficulty that they could be persuaded to remain with the expedition.

Next night they encamped at a spot where a stream fell into the Peace River from the north.

"Voila! w'at is dis?" exclaimed Ducette, as he leaped on shore.

"The fut-print of a grizzly bar," said Reuben, stooping to examine and measure the mark; "an oncommon big 'un, too full nine inches wide. I wouldn't like to embrace that bar."

The den, or place where this monster or some of its kindred had spent the winter, was also found not far-off. It was ten feet deep, horizontally, five feet high, and six feet wide.

"I wish we could find him," said Lawrence as he kindled the campfire.

"Ha! Swiftarrow has found something better," said Mackenzie, as the Indian strode into camp laden with the tongue, marrowbones, and other choice portions of an elk which he had killed a short distance down the river.

Lawrence had his wish next day, for they found a grizzly bear so fierce-looking and large that it was well for him he was in the canoe struggling with rapids at the time, for he was reckless enough to have attacked it single-handed a very dangerous proceeding, and a thing that the Indians never do. They appear to think that at least three men are necessary to the destruction of this much and justly feared monster of the mountains.

Lawrence looked at Bruin with a feeling of bloodthirsty desire; Bruin looked at Lawrence with an expression of stupid curiosity; and then slowly, not to say sulkily, retired into his native forest. Next day they beheld a more gratifying sight, namely, the snow-capped Rocky Mountains themselves, within the rugged portals of which their canoe passed not long afterwards. Here, as was to be expected, the river became narrower and more turbulent, and ere long the explorers had to face dangers and difficulties which tested their courage and endurance to the uttermost.

Chapter VIII

DIFFICULTIES AND DANGERS FACED AND OVERCOME.

Their entrance on the difficult navigation of the mountains was inaugurated by an accident to the canoe. It was a slight one, however, a rub against a rock which cracked the bark, and compelled them to land and spend an hour or so in mending it.

The current here was very strong, and creeping up along the banks was dangerous, owing to the masses of rock that frequently fell from the cliffs.

At one turn of the river in particular, a loud noise was heard, "Look out!" cried Mackenzie.

Before any one could well understand what danger threatened them, an enormous mass of rock was seen to bound down the banks right abreast of them, crashing through trees and bushes, and sending down showers of smaller stones. The men paddled with all their might, but the rock came straight at them, struck a flat piece of the cliff; and bursting like a bombshell, descended round them in a shower of small pieces, none of which, however, touched them, although many fell very near.

Coming one afternoon to a place where the current was stronger than usual, Mackenzie landed with Reuben, Lawrence, and Ducette, in order to lighten the canoe. They ascended the hills, which were covered with cypress, and but little encumbered with underwood. Here they found a beaten path, made either by Indians or wild animals. After walking a mile along it, they fell in with a herd of buffaloes with their young ones.

"Hist!" whispered Reuben, throwing forward the muzzle of his gun with the instinct of a hunter.

"Don't fire," said Mackenzie, arresting his arm; "it may alarm the natives, if any should chance to be within earshot. Send Wolf at them, Ducette."

Wolf, who belonged to Ducette, and had followed

his master, was a splendid fellow, not unlike the animal after which he had been named. He was well trained, too, and kept foot and tongue equally under command, until his master's wishes were made known. Hearing his name mentioned, he cocked his ears and gazed up in Ducette's face.

"Allons donc, Wolf," said Ducette.

Instantly, the dog made a magnificent rush into the midst of the herd, which scattered right and left, and seized a young calf by the nose! The creature, though young, was powerful, and for some time struggled bravely; but the hound held on with deadly firmness, and worried the calf to such an extent that in a short time Ducette was able to run in and despatch it.

To skin and dismember the carcase was a matter of little difficulty to these hunters, who were all expert butchers. They had just completed the work, and were congratulating each other on this accession of veal to the larder when a shot was heard in the direction of the canoe. It was immediately followed by another.

"The signal to recall us," said Mackenzie. "Gather up the meat, lads; come, be smart. Give them a couple of shots, Reuben, in reply."

The shots were fired, and, pushing down the hill through very close underwood, they soon came upon the canoe at the foot of a rapid which it was deemed impossible to ascend. What seemed impossible to some of his men, however, was by no means impossible to Mackenzie himself. He surveyed their position, saw that the succession of rapids above were indeed impracticable on that side of the river, but observed that on the other side it seemed possible to continue the ascent. The chief danger lay in attempting to cross with a heavy-laden canoe; but the attempt was made, and proved successful.

The dangers and mishaps which now assailed them in succession were enough to have dampened the ardour of the most resolute pioneer; but there are some natures which cannot be quelled, whose motto in all circumstances seem to be "Victory or death!" Of such a spirit was Alexander Mackenzie, although some of his men would fain have turned back. Indeed, the overcoming of their objection to proceed sometimes cost him more trouble than overcoming the difficulties of the navigation.

On reaching the other side of the river, they towed

the canoe along an island, and advanced well enough till they reached the extremity of it, when the line had to be exchanged for the paddles. In attempting to clear the point of the island, they were driven with great violence on a stony shore, and the frail canoe received considerable injury. To land and unload was the work of a few minutes; but it took a long time to repair the damage, by fitting in new pieces of bark and re-gumming the exposed seams. Part of the cargo, also, had to be opened and dried. This accomplished, they carried the whole across the point which had damaged them, reloaded and embarked. But it was now seen that it was not possible to advance farther up that side of the river either by paddling, hauling with the line, or pushing with poles. There remained only the alternative, therefore, of returning by the way they had come, or recrossing the river despite the strength of the current and the fact that there were several cascades just below them, to get into which would have involved canoe and men in certain destruction.

"Ve can nevair do it. Monsieur, dare not!" whispered Ducette to Reuben, as they floated for a few moments in an eddy.

Reuben glanced at his leader, who stood up in the canoe surveying the boiling rapids with a stern, intent gaze, and said quietly, "He'll try."

"Now, my lads, shove out with a will—ho!" said Mackenzie, sitting down.

Lawrence, who was steering, dipped his paddle vigorously, the men followed suit, the canoe shot into the stream, and in a moment gained the sheltering eddy below an island, which was shaped somewhat like a table with a thick centre leg or a mushroom. There were several such islands of solid rock in the river. They had been formed apparently by the action of the current doubtless also of ice cutting away their lower part, and leaving the mushroom-like tops, on which numbers of geese found a convenient breeding-place. From one to another of these islands the canoe shot in this way, thus decreasing the width of the final traverse. They paused a little longer at the last island, then shot into the stream, and, with a splendid sweep, gained the other side.

But here their case was little improved, for the current was almost as violent as that from which they had escaped. The craggy banks being low enough, however, to admit of the tracking-line being used, the men landed and towed the canoe till they came to the foot of the most rapid cascade they had yet seen. To ascend being impossible, they unloaded and carried everything over a rocky point; relaunched, reloaded, and continued to track with the line: but the dangers attending this operation had now seriously increased, for stones both small and great came continually rolling down the bank, and the steepness of the ground was such that the risk of the men slipping and falling into the water became imminent; besides which they had frequently to pass outside of trees which overhung the precipices; at such times a false step or a slip might have proved fatal. Presently, they came to a sheer impassable precipice, where the men had to embark and take to poling up the stream; but ere long they got into water too deep for the poles, and recourse was again had to the tracking-line. Coming to another precipice, they were again checked; but Mackenzie, finding that the rock was soft, cut steps in it for the distance of about twenty feet, and thus passing along, leaped, at the risk of his life, on a small rock below, where he received those who followed him on his shoulders. Thus four of them passed, and managed to drag up the canoe, though they damaged her in doing so. They had now reached a spot where the canoe could be repaired, and fortunately found a dead tree which had fallen from the cliffs above. But for this, fire could not have been kindled there, as no wood was to be procured within a mile of the place; in which case the repairs could not have been accomplished.

Thus yard by yard these hardy pioneers advanced by means of the line, the paddle, or the pole, sometimes carrying the lading, sometimes the canoe as well, and often within a hairbreadth of destruction. Indeed, nothing but the coolness, courage, and skill of all concerned could, under God, have brought them safely through the fatigues and dangers of that tremendous day.

But they had not yet done with it. Having surmounted these and many other difficulties, they reached a place where it became absolutely necessary to make a traverse across an unusually strong current. Here the men silently showed their estimate of the danger by stripping themselves to their shirts, that they might be the better prepared to swim for their lives, in case of accident to the canoe! Fortunately, the traverse was made successfully, and then at noon Mackenzie stopped and went ashore to take an altitude. While he was thus engaged, the men fastened the canoe and left it; but so insecure was the fastening that the current sheered her off, and if it had not happened that one of the men had remained in her and held on to the line, they would then and there have been deprived of every means of advancing or returning, as well as of present subsistence!

Despite the alarming nature of this incident, and the interference of a cloud that sought to neutralise the sun, our persevering traveller completed his observations, and proved the luckless spot to be situated in 56 degrees north latitude.

The rapidity of the current increased so much here, that in the distance of two miles they were compelled to unload four times and carry everything except the canoe; and even when thus light they found it difficult to prevent her being dashed to pieces against the rocks by the violence of the eddies.

The last danger they encountered was the worst. They came to a place where the river was nothing less than one continuous rapid, and they took everything out of the canoe, intending to tow her up with the line, only a few of the men being left in her. At length, however, the tumultuous heaving of the water was so great that a wave struck the canoe's bow and broke the line. The dismay of those on shore may be imagined, for now it seemed as if nothing could save their comrades from destruction; and certainly no human power did save them on that occasion; for, while they grasped the sides of the canoe helplessly, another wave drove them with a wild surge out of the tumbling water; so that the men were enabled to thrust her ashore; and, strange to say, though the frail vessel had been carried by tossing swells over rocks which were left naked a moment later, she had received no material injury.

This last accident, coupled with the fact that the river as far as they could see was a sheet of white foaming water, induced the leader of the band to give up all idea of advancing farther at that point by water.

But do not imagine, good reader, that this implied the desertion of the canoe. On the contrary, that accommodating vessel having hitherto carried our pioneers, they now proposed to carry it as shall be related presently.

Mackenzie met the grumbling discontent of his men with an order to ascend the hill and encamp there for the night.

"Vraiment—it all very easy to say go up dere and camp for de noit, mais I will go not farder!" growled Ducette, as he threw a heavy bag of provisions on his back and trudged sulkily up the hill.

The two young Indians evidently approved of this sentiment, and one or two of the other men seemed inclined to echo it; but Reuben and Lawrence laughed as they each shouldered a burden. The former said it was his firm conviction that nothing would, could, or should stop Monsieur Mackenzie but the Pacific Ocean.

The precipitous bank of the river, or "hill," up which they were desired to carry the tents, provisions, etcetera, necessary for their encampment, was so steep and encumbered with wood and scrub, that it might of itself have formed a sufficiently disheartening obstacle to men less accustomed to hardships; nevertheless, they braced themselves to it with wonted vigour, pushed through the scrub, felled trees to facilitate their ascent, and climbed like monkeys by the stems, until they gained the summit, where very soon a roaring fire was covered with bubbling kettles and broiling steaks and marrowbones.

Meanwhile Mackenzie, accompanied by Swiftarrow, went off on foot to survey the river ahead. He walked as long as daylight permitted, but found that there seemed to be no end to the rapids and cascades, and returned to camp with worn out moccasins and wounded feet. During the excursion he came on several old encampments of the Knisteneaux Indians, which must have been formed during war expeditions, a decided proof, he thought, of the savage and bloodthirsty nature of that people, seeing that their natural hunting grounds were very far removed from those almost inaccessible regions.

It now became too apparent to the leader of the expedition that the mountain at this place must be crossed on foot, with the canoe and its heavy lading on the shoulders of himself and his men; but before deciding on this course, he resolved to despatch Reuben and three men with the two Indian interpreters to proceed along the line of the river until they should reach a navigable part of it. Accordingly, next day this party set out. Mackenzie remained in camp to superintend the repairing of the canoe and take observations. He was successful in obtaining correct time, and found the latitude to be 56 degrees 8 minutes.

At sunset the exploring party returned. They had penetrated the thick woods, ascended hills, descended valleys, and had finally got above the rapids, a distance of about three leagues; but their account of the difficulties in the way of advancing was very discouraging indeed. Mackenzie had foreseen this, and had made suitable preparations to counteract the evil effects thereof. In their absence he had prepared for them an enormous kettle of wild rice highly sweetened with sugar. When the tired, hungry, and footsore men sat down to this they became quite willing to listen to their leader's arguments in favour of a bold advance, and when the hearty supper was washed down with a liberal allowance of rum, and finished off with a pipe, they avowed themselves ready to face anything! In this satisfactory state of mind they retired to rest, while their leader sat up in the hope of obtaining an observation of Jupiter and his first satellite, which laudable aim was frustrated by cloudy weather.

Chapter IX

DEEPER AND DEEPER INTO THE UNKNOWN WILDERNESS.

Next day the arduous work of cutting a road through the forest and up the mountainside was begun.

At daybreak their leader assembled the men. "Now, my lads," said he, "the work before us for the next two or three days will be very stiff, but it would be a disgrace to us if after having come so far, we were so soon only a little beyond the middle of May to give in because of a few difficulties. Besides, I am strongly of opinion that we cannot now be far from the height of land, and you know well enough that the moment we set foot on the other side of the topmost ridge of the mountains it will be all down stream. Let us set to work, then, with a will. Take your axes and cut your way through everything. The trees here are, as you see, of small growth. Cut those of them that stand conveniently in such a way as that they shall fall parallel with the intended road, but don't sever them quite through so that they make a sort of railing on each side. Come, Lawrence, I'm glad to see that you are ready to begin, like a good pioneer show them an example."

Lawrence, who was the only one of the listening band who chanced to have his axe on his shoulder, smiled when thus addressed, and, turning around, exclaimed "Voila!" as he swayed the axe aloft and sent it sweeping at one stroke through a young tree, which fell with a crash and covered half of the party with its branches.

A general laugh followed, and immediately the whole band set to work with their axes, headed by Mackenzie himself.

From early morning till sunset they toiled during the next three days, almost without cessation, except for meals. They cut their way from the margin of the river, where the rocks and ground shelved so steeply

that one false step of any of the men would have been
followed by a headlong plunge into the water. Over
the ridge, and down into a hollow beyond, and up
the mountain farther on, they hewed a broad track,
by which they conveyed the baggage and then carried
up the canoe. This latter was an extremely difficult
operation at the first part of the road, requiring the
united efforts of the whole party. Being lifted on the
shoulders of some of the men, the tracking-rope was
fastened to the bow, and others of the party went
in advance and took a couple of turns of the rope
round a stump. The bearers then advanced steadily
up the steep side of the mountain till they reached
those who, by holding on to the rope, relieved them
of any downward weight. The rope was then shifted to
a stump farther up, and the advance was continued.
Thus, they may be said to have warped the canoe up
the mountain! By two in the afternoon everything
was got to the summit. Then Mackenzie, axe in hand,
led the way forward. The progress was slow, the work
exhausting. Through every species of country they cut
their way. Here the trees were large and the ground
encumbered with little underwood; there, the land

was strewn with the trunks of fallen timber, where fire had passed with desolating power years before, and in its place had sprung up extensive copses of so close a growth, and so choked up with briars, that it was all but impossible to cut through them. Poplar, birch, cypress, red pine, spruce, willow, alder, arrowwood, red-wood, hard, and other trees, all fell before the bright axes of the voyageurs, with gooseberry bushes, currant bushes, briars, and other shrubs innumerable. It must not be supposed that they did this heavy work with absolute impunity. No, there was many a bruise and blow from falling trees, and even the shrubs were successful not only in tearing trousers and leggings, but also in doing considerable damage to skin and flesh. So toilsome was the labour, that at the close of one of the days they had advanced only three miles.

On the afternoon of the third day they finally came out in triumph on the banks of the river above the cascades, having cut a road of about nine miles in extent.

Once again, then, behold them afloat and paddling up stream still westward with hopes animated and fortune smiling, or, as Reuben put it, with "a gale of luck blowin' right astarn." Reuben, be it observed, had consorted with sailors in his day down the Gulf of St. Lawrence, and had picked up a little of their slang.

But their good fortune never lasted long at a time. Their progress being very slow, it was found advisable to send the young Indian interpreters on shore to lighten the canoe and to hunt as they advanced. They frequently killed elk and other game. On one of these occasions Swiftarrow was nearly killed. He had been sent to fetch the choice parts of an elk which they had shot, when a big rock fell from the cliffs above, and was dashed to pieces at his very feet. Just after this incident a violent fall of rain took place, obliging them to remain in camp for a day. Then driftwood barred the river, and an opening had to be forced through it. Then more cascades appeared to check their advance; and, worst of all, just as they began to hope that the height of land was gained, an opening in the hills revealed a range of blue mountains far ahead of them, running south and north as far as the eye could reach. To add to their perplexities, they came to a fork in the river, one branch running due west, the other in a southerly direction.

"Follow the westerly branch," said one; "that must be the right one."

"Not so sure o' that," observed Reuben; "the end of a track don't needsesarly p'int out the gin'ral run of it."

"You are right, Reuben," said Mackenzie; "besides, I have been warned of this very branch by an old Indian whom I met last winter, and who said he had been up here in his youth. Therefore, though appearances are against it, I shall follow the southern branch."

Mackenzie was right in this determination, as it afterwards proved, but most of his men grumbled very much at the time, because the southerly branch, besides appearing to be the wrong one, was a very rapid and dangerous stream. They knew by that time, however, that nothing could bend their leader's will, so they submitted, though with a bad grace.

Here an immense number of beaver were seen, and a gladsome sight it was to the furtrader, because beaver skins at that time were in great repute silk hats not having, as yet, beaten them off the field and reduced their value to almost nothing. In some places these sagacious and busy animals had cut down several acres of large poplars. At this place, too, they had an alarm, some of the men declaring that they had heard shots fired by Indians in the woods. A whole night was therefore spent on the *qui vive*, although it turned out to be a false alarm.

One morning, the weather being fine and the river more manageable than usual, Mackenzie landed with Reuben and the two Indians, to ascend an adjacent mountain, telling his men to proceed in the canoe diligently, and directing them to fire two shots if they should require his return, agreeing that he would do the same if he should wish them to wait for him. Nothing was gained by this attempt to obtain a better prospect. On descending to the river they fired two shots, as agreed on, but no answer was received. Again they tried it, but the deep silence was only broken by an echo and by the rushing of the river.

"They're behind us," suggested Reuben.

"They've overshot us," said the Indians.

Again two shots were fired, but still no reply came. Mackenzie's mind was at once filled with anxious fears lest some accident should have befallen his canoe, while he reproached himself for having left them even for a brief period in such dangerous navigation.

In these circumstances he turned to consult with his men.

"It's my opinion," said Reuben, "that they've diskivered more rapids than they bargained for, and are out of earshot behind us; so we'd better make tracks down stream till we find 'em."

"Not so," said the elder of the Indians; "without doubt the canoe is dashed to pieces, and our comrades are even now with their forefathers. We shall see them no more; and my advice is that we construct a raft and try to return on it to the lands whence we came."

Anxious though he was, Mackenzie could scarce refrain from laughing at the prompt way in which the red man had consigned his comrades to destruction. "Come," said he, "we won't give them up quite so readily as you seem inclined to. We shall make at least one effort to find them."

It was now arranged that Reuben and one of the Indians should remain at the spot where they then were, kindle a large fire, and send branches down the stream from time to time, as a signal to their comrades if they chanced to be below, and that Mackenzie with the other Indian should walk up the bank of the river several miles. This was done; but they returned after some hours to the fire, having seen nothing of the canoe.

As evening was now approaching, they became thoroughly alarmed, and a more rigorous plan of search was instituted. Reuben was sent off with one Indian to proceed down the river as far as he could go before night came on, with directions to continue the journey in the morning as far as to the place where they had encamped the preceding evening. Mackenzie with the other Indian again went off up the river, intending to make a thorough search in that direction. They had no food with them, but, having their guns and the means of making fire, they had no anxiety on that score, except in regard to an immediate meal, for game was scarcer than usual at that particular spot.

It was agreed that if both should fail of success, they were to return to the place where they then separated. But their anxieties were brought to an end sooner than they had hoped for. Not very long after parting, Mackenzie heard a very far-off shot, and then another, and in a few minutes an answering double shot at a still greater distance. These being the concerted signals, he knew that the canoe party must have been discovered by Reuben; he therefore retraced his steps with a light heart, despite the fact that he had worn the moccasins off his feet, and was completely drenched with rain. It turned out that the delay had been occasioned by the breaking of the canoe, and the consequent necessity of landing to repair damages. Indeed, the sorely-battered craft had become almost a wreck. As a fitting climax to this disastrous day, the night finished off with thunder, lightning, and rain.

While thus forcing their way to the head-waters of the river, they met with a small party of miserable looking natives, who received them at first with violent demonstrations of an intention to immolate them on the spot if they should dare to land. It was evident that the poor creatures had been subjected to bad treatment and deception by other and more powerful tribes, because they remained in a state of great suspicion and anxiety even after the interpreter had stated earnestly that the intentions of the white men were friendly, and after gifts had been presented to them. By degrees, however, they became more confident, and as their anxieties diminished their curiosity increased.

"I do believe," said Lawrence, "that the critters have never seen white folk before."

To most people it might have seemed ridiculous to have heard that bronzed voyageur calling himself and his brown-faced, smoke-dried, weather worn companions, by the title of white people; but Lawrence referred to the natural colour of the race to which he belonged.

"They do seem rather koorious," observed Reuben, as one of the Indians timidly touched his arm and looked wonderingly up into his blue eyes.

It was found, however, that these natives had heard of white people, though they had not seen them; moreover, they displayed a number of knives and iron implements which they said had been procured from people inhabiting the banks of a river which might be reached over a carrying-place of "eleven days in length," and which river flowed in an opposite direction from the Peace River. These people, they said, travelled during a moon to get to the country of another tribe who dwelt in houses, and these again extended their journeys to the sea, or, as they called it, the "Stinking Lake," where they exchanged their furs with white people, like our pioneers, who came to the coast of that lake in canoes as big as islands!

Here, then, at last, was definite information, and the enterprising discoverer was not long in availing himself of it. After gratifying his new friends with sundry little gifts, a feed of pemmican, which they relished amazingly, and a taste of sugar to tickle their palates, he gained their confidence so much as to induce one of them to be his guide, and immediately pushed forward.

In the course of the following week they gained the much-longed-for height of land, and found two lakelets within a quarter of a mile of each other, from one of which the waters find their way through Peace River, on the east side of the mountains, into the Arctic Sea, while from the other the waters flow south and west through the great River Columbia to the Pacific Ocean.

But the succession of disasters that befell them here, and the difficulties of the route for it could not be called navigation threw all their previous experiences into the shade. One day, having made a portage, they relaunched the canoe and began the well-nigh forgotten process of descending stream. They had not gone far when they struck a rock and were driven down sideways with great violence, Mackenzie, followed by his men, jumped into the shallow to turn the canoe straight, but in a moment the water deepened and they had to scramble inboard again hurriedly. Swiftarrow by some mischance was left behind to struggle on shore as best he might. Before they could resume their paddles they struck again; the stem of the canoe was shattered like an egg-shell and hung only by the gunwales, so that Lawrence, who was steering, had to quit his place. The violence of the stroke drove them to the opposite side of the river, where the bow met with the same fate. At that moment Reuben seized the branches of a small overhanging tree in a desperate hope of checking the canoe, but the tree proved so elastic that he was jerked on shore in an instant as if by magic, and the canoe swept over a cascade, where several holes were broken in her bottom and nearly all the bars started. At the same moment the wreck fell flat on the water; all the men jumped out, and Ducette, whose courage forsook him, shouted, "Save yourselves!"

"Not so! Hold on to the canoe, men," cried Mackenzie sternly. The men obeyed, and thus prevented the total loss of everything. Yard by yard, on the verge of destruction they waded down the rapid, and guided the wreck into shallow water, where some held her fast while the others, who were quickly joined by Reuben and Swiftarrow, carried the lading safely ashore. On this occasion several things were lost, the chief of these being their whole stock of bullets, but they had plenty of shot left from which ball could be made.

One might have thought this was at last sufficient to have turned them back so at least thought most of the men, who began to look rebellious but Mackenzie partly compelled, partly encouraged them to advance. The canoe was dragged ashore and repaired, or rather reconstructed, and eventually through indescribable difficulties he reached the navigable stream which forms the headwaters of the Columbia River. This he descended a considerable distance, and met with many of the natives, who told him that the country below abounded with game and the river with fish; but as the course of the latter ran towards the south, and the distance by it to the sea was described as being extremely great, he deemed it advisable to retrace his course a short way and then strike westward overland to the Pacific.

The old canoe being now little better than a wreck, birchbark was procured and a new canoe built, after which the stream was ascended until a spot was reached where the natives were in the habit of starting overland for the sea coast. Here the canoe was hidden, an Indian guide procured, and then these indomitable pioneers prepared to cross the wilderness on foot.

Chapter X

We follow our travellers now over the last portion of their trying journey. Well would it have been for them if they could have followed their route as easily as you and I, reader, follow them in imagination. Over mountain and swamp, through forest and brake, in heat and in cold, sunshine and rain, they plodded wearily but resolutely on towards the far west, until they reached the farthest west of all, where the great continent dips into the greater Pacific.

At starting on this overland route they buried some provisions, and putting in a place of security their canoe and such stores as they did not require or could not carry, they set out, each man laden with a burden varying from forty-five to ninety pounds weight, besides arms and ammunition. They were led by an Indian guide with several of his relations, and followed by their dog Wolf. This guide was deemed necessary, not so much to show the way as to introduce them to the various tribes through whose territory they should have to pass.

It takes a large portion of a quarto volume to recount their interesting adventures by the way. How then, can we presume to attempt a fair narrative in a few pages? The thing is impossible. We can but refer our readers to Mackenzie's ponderous journal, in which, embedded amongst a mass of important details, will be found a record of one of the most interesting voyages ever undertaken.

As a matter of course difficulties assailed them at the outset. This would seem to be the universal experience of pioneers. Game latterly had begun to grow scarce, so that, their provisions being low, they were obliged to go on short allowance two meals a day. Their food, being pemmican, required no cooking. Mingled heat, mosquitoes, sandflies, and a rugged country, with short commons, and danger, as well as worry from savages, was the beginning and pretty much the middle and end of their experience. They were soon joined by an elderly man and three other natives, and not only did these three Indians, but all the others along the route, harass them by their caprice, unfaithfulness, and childish petulance, and self-will.

One day their guide resolved to leave them; then, without being solicited to stay, he changed his mind and went on with them. Again, one night, at a time when they were anxious not to lose him, Mackenzie, who knew he meant to take leave quietly, asked him to sleep with him. He willingly consented, the white man's cloak being a snug covering, and thus was he guarded! but his guardian suffered severe consequences owing to the filthy state of the Indian, whose garments were indescribable, his body being smeared with red earth, and his hair with fish-oil!

Coming to a lake they observed the sky grow very black. "A thunderstorm brewin'," suggested Reuben.

"Encamp, and up with the tent, boys," said Mackenzie.

The tent! It was a misnomer, their only shelter being

a sheet of thin oiled cloth and the overhanging trees. Down came a deluge that kept them very close for a time; then, on resuming the march, the guide was requested to go in advance and brush the water off the bushes, but he coolly declined. Mackenzie himself therefore undertook the duty. During this storm the ground was rendered white with hailstones as large as a musket ball. The third day they met natives who received them well. These were going to the great river to fish, and seemed unlike many other tribes to venerate age, for they carried on their backs by turns a poor old woman who was quite blind and infirm. Farther on they met other Indians on their way to the same great river, which abounded with salmon. These told them that they would soon reach a river, neither large nor long, which entered an arm of the sea, and where a great wooden canoe with white people was said to be frequently seen!

"Here is encouragement for us; let us push on," said Mackenzie. "Push on," echoed Reuben and Lawrence and some of the other men; but some grumbled at the hardships they had to endure, and the short allowance of provisions, while the Indians threatened to desert them.

Mackenzie must have had something very peculiar in his look and manner, for he seemed to possess the faculty of saying little in reply to his men, and yet of constraining them to follow him. Doubtless, had some one else written his journal we should have learned the secret. It seems as if, when rebellion was looking blackest and the storm about to burst, instead of commanding or disputing, he calmly held his tongue and went off to take an observation of the sun, and on that process being completed, he almost invariably found his men in a more tractable condition! Occasionally, we read of quiet remonstrance or grave reasoning, and frequently of hearty encouragement and wise counsel, but never of violence, although he was sorely tried. Perchance they knew that he was dangerous to trifle with! We cannot tell, but certainly he seems to have been a splendid manager of men.

At last they reached an Indian village where they were hospitably entertained, and presented with as much roasted salmon as they required. These people lived almost exclusively on fish and berries; were more cleanly than other tribes, and apparently less addicted to war or hunting. Here two new guides were obtained, and the people conciliated with gifts of beads, knives, and other trinkets.

Leaving them they spent a wretched night on the shores of a lake, deluged with rain and tormented with sandflies and mosquitoes the former being perhaps the greatest pests of the country. Soon the guides grew tired of their mode of travelling, and the allowance of provisions had to be still further reduced. Fearing that they might run short altogether, Mackenzie ordered Reuben and his son to fall behind, bury some pemmican in reserve for their return, and make a fire over the spot to conceal the fact that it had been dug into. They were now on two-thirds of their regular allowance. Soon afterwards they came to a river too deep to ford, but one of their guides swam across and brought over a raft that lay on the other side. This ferried most of them over, but Swiftarrow and some of the others preferred to swim across.

At length, after many days of suffering and toil they crossed the last range of mountains and began to descend. Here magnificent cedars and other trees were seen, some of the former being fully eighteen feet in circumference. The natives whom they met with were sometimes stern, sometimes kind, but always suspicious at first. The soothing effects of gifts, however, were pretty much the same in all. Still the party had several narrow escapes.

On one occasion Mackenzie, when alone, was surrounded and seized, but he soon freed himself, and just at that moment when his life seemed to hang on a hair, Reuben Guff happened to come up, and the natives took to flight. Some of these natives were very expert canoe men, caught salmon by means of weirs, dwelt in wooden houses elevated on poles, boiled their food in watertight baskets by putting red-hot stones into them, made cakes of the inner rind of the hemlock sprinkled with oil, and seemed to have a rooted antipathy to flesh of every kind. Some of the salmon they caught were fully forty pounds' weight. The chief of one tribe said that, ten years before, he had gone down to the sea in a large canoe, and there had met with two large vessels full of white men who treated him very kindly. These, Mackenzie concluded, must have been the ships of Captain Cook, an opinion which was strengthened by the discovery that the chief's canoe was ornamented with sea otter's teeth, which bear some resemblance to human teeth, for which they had been mistaken by the great navigator. At last, on the 20th of July, the heroic perseverance of Mackenzie met with its reward. On that day he obtained a canoe, and descending a river, entered an arm of the Pacific! He did not himself, indeed, deem the object of the expedition attained until he had battled on for a couple of days longer in the face of the opposition of his own men and hostility of the natives and had obtained reliable observations which settled beyond all dispute, his exact position on the globe. But to all intents and purposes he had accomplished his great object on that day, namely, the crossing of the American Wilderness to the Pacific Ocean.

Even in the midst of his triumph this long-enduring man was worried by petty trials, for one of the Indian guides took it into his head to desert. As he was the son of a chief, and, it was to be feared, might prejudice the natives against them, Reuben Guff was directed to pursue him. That worthy took with him Swiftarrow, and exerting his long sinewy legs to the utmost, soon overtook the fugitive and brought him back. But it was no part of Mackenzie's plan to tyrannise over men. He received the deserter kindly, gave him a pair of moccasins, some provisions, a silk handkerchief, and some good advice, and then sent him back to his friends. The other Indian who remained with them succeeded about the same time in killing a large porcupine, which was very acceptable to all—especially to its captor, who ate so largely of it as to be obliged to undergo a prolonged period of repose in order to sleep it off.

At length, being in a state of semi-starvation, with a leaky canoe, and unfriendly natives around, Mackenzie took a last observation, which gave 52 degrees 20 minutes 48 second North latitude and 128 degrres 2 minutes West longitude.

Then he turned his face eastward. Before quitting the coast, however, a smooth rock was selected and thereon was written, in large letters, with a mixture of melted grease and vermilion, this brief memorial, "Alexander Mackenzie, from Canada, by land, the twenty-second of July, one thousand seven hundred and ninety-three."

The return journey was scarcely less arduous than

the outward, but they undertook it with the knowledge that every step carried them nearer home, and with the exhilarating consciousness that their labours had been crowned with success. Besides this, they now knew what lay before them each day as far as the route was concerned and at the various places where provisions had been secreted the party was strengthened and enabled to advance with greater vigour. On arriving at the Great River they found their canoe, goods, and provisions just as they had left them about five weeks before. Here they made preparations for proceeding to the head waters of the Columbia River, crossing over to those of the Peace River, and so returning by the way they had come. In order to mark this happy point in the expedition, Mackenzie treated himself and men to a dram, "but," observe that I quote his words, reader,"we had been so long without tasting any spirituous liquor, that we had Lost all relish for it!" Rejoice in that testimony, ye teetotallers. Think of it, ye topers. Put it in your pipes, ye smokers and make the most of it!

"Nearing home at last, boys," said Mackenzie many weeks afterwards, as, having descended the turbulent

Peace River, they rounded a point of land and came in sight of their old winter quarters; "shake out the flag, and give them a volley and a cheer."

The men obeyed, and were in such high spirits, and made such active use of their paddles, that they reached the landing place before the two men who had been left there in the spring, could recover their senses sufficiently to answer their questions! But this was not home yet. Some days had still to elapse ere these toil-worn men could lay aside their paddles and rest their wearied limbs.

At last, after an absence of eleven months, they reached Fort Chipewyan, where their leader resumed the duties of the furtrade, and Swiftarrow once more kissed the brown cheek of Darkeye, who filled his heart with grim delight by placing in his paternal arms a soft, round, fat, little brown female baby, with eyes as dark and bright as her own, and a nose which was a miniature facsimile of its father's.

One week after their arrival, Reuben and Lawrence, Swiftarrow and Darkeye, entered Mackenzie's room to bid him farewell.

"I'm sorry you are bent on leaving me," said their

former leader; "but you have the satisfaction of knowing that you have contributed greatly to the success of our two expeditions. You have indeed proved yourselves able pioneers."

"Thank'ee, sir," said Reuben, while a quiet smile of satisfaction lighted up his grave features. "It was all along a hobby o' mine, an' of Lawrence, too, to do a bit o' diskivery; an' now we're content—for it ain't possible, I fancy, to do much more in that line than push your canoe into the Frozen Sea on the one hand, or the Pacific on the other. It's harder work than I thowt it would be though I didn't expect child's play neither; an' it's our opinion, sir, that you are the only man in the country as could have done it at all. We intend now to go back to the settlements. As for the redskin," he added, glancing at Swiftarrow, "he ha'n't got no ambition one way or another as to diskivery; but he's a good and true man, nevertheless, you'll allow. And now, sir, farewell. May a blessing from above rest on you and yours."

Saying this the bold backwoodsman shook Mackenzie by the hand and left the room. Every one in the fort was on the bank to bid them farewell. Silently they stepped into their canoe, and in a few minutes had paddled out of sight into the great wilderness of wood and water.

Reader, our tale, if such it may be styled, is told. As for the hero whose steps for a time we have so closely followed, he became one of the most noted traders, as he was now one of the most celebrated discoverers, in North America. He afterwards became for a time the travelling companion in America of the Duke of Kent, father of Queen Victoria; was knighted in acknowledgment of his great and important achievements; married one of Scotland's fair daughters; and finally died in the midst of his native Highland hills, leaving behind him a volume which as we said at the beginning—proves him to have been one of the most vigorous, persevering, manly, and successful pioneers that ever traversed the continent of North America.

THE END.

Appendix

EXTRACT OF LETTER REFERRED TO ON PAGE 42.

From William Mackenzie, Esquire, of Gairloch, to George Mackenzie, Esquire, of Avoch, dated Leamington, 24th May 1856.

When in Stockholm in 1824, Lord Blomfield, our Minister there, did me the honour of presenting me to the King, Bernadotte, father of the present King of Sweden.

At the King's special request, the audience was a private one, and I was further especially requested to oblige by coming in my full Highland dress. The audience lasted fully an hour. Such an interest did Napoleon's first and most fortunate Marshal take in everything that was Highland, not even the skiandhu escaped him.

I now come to your family portion of the audience.

As we chatted on, old Bernadotte (leaning familiarly upon my O'Keachan claymore) was pleased to say in that suaviter in modo for which his eagle eye so fitted him, "Yes, I repeat it, you Highlanders are deservedly proud of your country. Your forefathers and your people are a race apart, distinct from all the rest of Britain in high moral as well as martial bearing, and long, I hope, may you feel and show it outwardly by this noble distinction in dress. But allow me to observe, Sir, that in your family name, in the name of Mackenzie, there is a very predominant lustre, which shall never be obliterated from my mind. Pray, are you connected in any way with Sir Alexander Mackenzie, the celebrated North American traveller, whose name and researches are immortalised by his discoveries in the Arctic Ocean, and of the river which since then does honour to his name?" I informed His Majesty that as a boy I had known him well, and that our family and his were nearly connected. This seemed to give me still greater favour with him, for, familiarly putting his hand on my shoulder brooch, he replied that on that account alone his making my acquaintance gave him greater satisfaction. He then proceeded to tell Lord Blomfield and me how your father's name had become familiar to him, and so much valued in his eyes. He said that at one time Napoleon had arranged to distract the affairs of Britain by attacking her in her Canadian possessions not by a direct descent upon them, but by a route which men expected would take England quite by surprise and prove infallible.

That route was to be up the Mississippi, Ohio, etcetera, up to our Canadian border lakes. For this arrangements were to be made with America, New Orleans occupied as a *pied a terre* by France, etcetera, etcetera. The organisation and command of this gigantic enterprise, as Bernadotte said, "was given to me by the Emperor, with instructions to make myself master of every work which could bear upon it, and the facilities the nature of the country afforded. Foremost amongst these the work of your namesake (Sir Alexander Mackenzie) was recommended, but how to get at it, with all communications with England interdicted, all knowledge of English unknown to me, seemed a difficulty not easily to be got over. However, as every one knows, my then master, l'Empereur, was not the man to be overcome by such small difficulties. The book, a huge quarto, was procured through the smugglers, and in an inconceivably short space of time most admirably translated into French for my especial use. [A copy of this translation was found in Napoleon's library at St. Helena.] I need hardly say with what interest I perused and reperused that admirable work, till I had made myself so thoroughly master of it that I could almost fancy myself," this he said laughing heartily, "taking your Canadas en revers from the upper waters; and ever since I have never ceased to look upon the name and think of the author with more than ordinary respect and esteem."

After a short pause and a long-drawn breath, almost amounting to a sigh, accompanied by a look at Blomfield and a most expressive "*Ah, milord, que de changes depuis ces jours-la,*" Bernadotte concluded by saying that the Russian campaign had knocked that of Canada on the head until Russia was crushed! but it had pleased God to ordain it otherwise, "*et maintenant* *me voila Roi de Suede,"*his exact words as he concluded these compliments to your father.

Fast in the Ice

FIGHTING A POLAR BEAR—Page 289

Fast In The Ice

ADVENTURES IN THE POLAR REGIONS

by

R.M. BALLANTYNE

Author of
The Pioneers, The Island Queen,
The Cannibal Islands, etc., etc.

THE VISION FORUM, INC.
SAN ANTONIO, TEXAS

CONTENTS

Chapter I

One day, many years ago, a brig cast off from her moorings, and sailed from a British port for the Polar Seas. That brig never came back.

Many a hearty cheer was given, many a kind wish was uttered, many a handkerchief was waved, and many a tearful eye gazed that day as the vessel left Old England, and steered her course into the unknown regions of the far north.

But no cheer ever greeted her return; no bright eyes ever watched her homeward-bound sails rising on the far-off horizon.

Battered by the storms of the Arctic seas, her sails and cordage stiffened by the frosts, and her hull rasped and shattered by the ice of those regions, she was forced on a shore where the green grass has little chance to grow, where winter reigns nearly all the year round, where man never sends his merchandise, and never drives his plough. There the brig was frozen in; there, for two long years, she lay unable to move, and her starving crew forsook her; there, year after year, she lay, unknown, unvisited by civilised man, and unless the wild Eskimos have torn her to pieces, and made spears of her timbers, or the ice has swept her out to sea and whirled her to destruction, there she lies still—hard and fast in the ice.

The vessel was lost, but her crew were saved, and most of them returned to tell their kinsfolk of the wonders and the dangers of the frozen regions, where God has created some of the most beautiful and some of the most awful objects that were ever looked on by the eye of man.

What was told by the fireside, long ago, is now recounted in this book.

Imagine a tall, strong man, of about five-and-forty,

with short, curly black hair, just beginning to turn grey; stern black eyes, that look as if they could pierce into your secret thoughts; a firm mouth, with lines of good-will and kindness lurking about it; a deeply-browned skin, and a short, thick beard and moustache. That is a portrait of the commander of the brig. His name was Harvey. He stood on the deck, close by the wheel, looking wistfully over the stern. As the vessel bent before the breeze, and cut swiftly through the water, a female hand was raised among the gazers on the pier, and a white scarf waved in the breeze. In the forefront of the throng, and lower down, another hand was raised; it was a little one, but very vigorous; it whirled a cap round a small head of curly black hair, and a shrill "hurrah!" came floating out to sea.

The captain kissed his hand and waved his hat in reply; then, wheeling suddenly round, he shouted, in a voice of thunder:

"Mind your helm, there; let her away a point. Take a pull on these foretopsail halyards; look alive, lads!"

"Aye, aye, sir!" replied the men.

There was no occasion whatever for these orders. The captain knew that well enough, but he had his own reasons for giving them. The men knew that, too, and they understood his reasons when they observed the increased sternness of his eyes, and the compression of his lips.

Inclination and duty! What wars go on in the hearts of men—high and low, rich and poor—between these two. What varied fortune follows man, according as the one or the other carries the day.

"Please, sir," said a gruff, broad-shouldered, and extremely short man, with little or no forehead, a hard, vacant face, and a pair of enormous red whiskers; "please, sir, Sam Baker's took very bad; I think it would be as well if you could give him a little physic, sir; a tumbler of Epsom, or some-think of that sort."

"Why, Mr. Dicey, there can't be anything very far wrong with Baker," said the captain, looking down at his second mate; "he seems to me one of the healthiest men in the ship. What's the matter with him?"

"Well, I can't say, sir," replied Mr. Dicey, "but he looks horrible bad, all yellow and green about the gills, and fearful red round the eyes. But what frightens me most is that I heard him groanin' very heavy about a quarter of an hour ago, and then I saw him suddenly fling himself into his 'ammock and begin blubberin' like a child. Now, sir, I say, when a grow'd-up man gives way like that, there must be some-think far wrong with his inside. And it's a serious thing, sir, to take a sick man on such a voyage as this."

"Does he not say what's wrong with him?" asked the captain.

"No, sir; he don't. He says it's nothin', and he'll be all right if he's only let alone. I did hear him once or twice muttering some-think about his wife and child; you know, sir, he's got a young wife, and she had a baby about two months 'fore we came away, but I can't think that's got much to do with it, for I've got a wife myself, sir, and six children, two of 'em bein' babies, and that don't upset *me*, and Baker's a much stronger man."

"You are right, Mr. Dicey, he is a much stronger man than you," replied the captain, "and I doubt not that his strength will enable him to get over this without the aid of physic."

"Very well, sir," said Mr. Dicey.

The second mate was a man whose countenance never showed any signs of emotion, no matter what he felt. He seldom laughed, or, if he did, his mouth remained almost motionless, and the sounds that came out were anything but cheerful. He had light grey eyes which always wore an expression of astonishment; but the expression was accidental; it indicated no feeling. He would have said, "Very well, sir," if the captain had refused to give poor Baker food instead of physic.

"And hark'ee, Mr. Dicey," said the captain, "don't let him be disturbed till he feels inclined to move."

"Very well, sir," replied the second mate, touching his cap as he turned away.

"So," murmured the captain, as he gazed earnestly at the now distant shore, "I'm not the only one who carries a heavy heart to sea this day and leaves sorrowing hearts behind him."

Chapter II

AT SEA—THE FIRST STORM.

It is now hundreds of years since the North polar regions began to attract general attention. Men have long felt very inquisitive about that part of the earth, and many good ships, many noble lives have been lost in trying to force a passage through the ice that encumbers the Arctic seas, summer and winter. Britain has done more than other nations in the cause of discovery within the Arctic circle. The last and greatest of her Arctic heroes perished there—the famous Sir John Franklin.

Were I writing a history of those regions I would

have much to say of other countries as well as of our own. But such is not my object in this book. I mean simply to follow in the wake of one of Britain's adventurous discoverers, and thus give the reader an idea of the fortunes of those gallant men who risk life and limb for the sake of obtaining knowledge of distant lands.

There have always been restless spirits in this country. There have ever been men who, when boys, were full of mischief, and who could "settle to nothing" when they grew up. Lucky for us, lucky for the world, that such is the case! Many of our "restless spirits," as we call them, have turned out to be our heroes, our discoverers, our greatest men. No doubt many of them have become our drones, our sharpers, our blacklegs. But that is just saying that some men are good, while others are bad—no blame is due to what is called the restlessness of spirit. Our restless men, if good, find rest in action; in bold energetic toil; if bad, they find rest, alas! in untimely graves.

Captain Harvey was one of our restless spirits. He had a deeply learned friend who said to him one day that he felt sure *"there was a sea of open water round the North Pole!"* Hundreds of ships had tried to reach that pole without success, because they always found a barrier of thick ice raised against them. This friend said that if a ship could only cut or force its way through the ice to a certain latitude north, open water would be found. Captain Harvey was much interested in this. He could not rest until he had proved it. He had plenty of money, so had his friend. They resolved to buy a vessel and send it to the seas lying within the Arctic circle. Other rich friends helped them; a brig was bought, it was named the *Hope*, and, as we have seen in the last chapter, it finally set sail under command of Captain Harvey.

Many days and nights passed, and the *Hope* kept her course steadily toward the coast of North America. Greenland was the first land they hoped to see. Baffin's Bay was the strait through which they hoped to reach the open polar sea.

The *Hope* left England as a whaler, with all the boats, lances, harpoons, lines, and other apparatus used in the whale fishery. It was intended that she should do a little business in that way if Captain Harvey thought it advisable, but the discovery of new lands and seas was their chief end and aim.

At first the weather was fine, the wind fair, and the voyage prosperous. But one night there came a deep calm. Not a breath of air moved over the sea, which was as clear and polished as a looking-glass. The captain walked the deck with the surgeon of the ship, a nephew of his own, named Gregory.

Tom Gregory was a youth of about nineteen, who had not passed through the whole course of a doctor's education, but who was a clever fellow, and better able to cut and carve and physic poor suffering humanity than many an older man who wrote MD after his name. He was a fine, handsome, strapping fellow, with a determined manner and a kind heart. He was able to pull an oar with the best man aboard, and could even steer the brig in fine weather, if need be. He was hearty and romantic, and a great favourite with the men. He, too, was a restless spirit. He had grown tired of college life, and had made up his mind to take a year's run into the Polar regions, by way of improving his knowledge of the "outlandish" parts of the world.

"I don't like the look of the sky to-day, Tom," said the captain, glancing at the horizon and then at the sails.

"Indeed!" said Tom, in surprise. "It seems to me the most beautiful afternoon we have had since the voyage began. But I suppose you seamen are learned in signs which we landsmen do not understand."

"Perhaps we are," replied the captain; "but it does not require much knowledge of the weather to say that such a dead calm as this, and such unusual heat, is not likely to end in a gentle breeze."

"You don't object to a stiff breeze, uncle?" said the youth.

"No, Tom; but I don't like a storm, because it does us no good, and may do us harm."

"Storms do you no good, uncle!" cried Tom; "how can you say so? Why, what is it that makes our sailors such trumps? The British tar would not be able to face danger as he does if there were no storms."

"True, Tom, but the British tar would not require to face danger at all if there were no storms. What says the barometer, Mr. Mansell?" said the captain, looking down the skylight into the cabin, where the first mate—a middle-sized man of thirty-five, or thereabouts—was seated at the table writing up the ship's log-book.

"The glass has gone down an inch, sir, and is still falling," answered the mate.

"Reef the topsail, Mr. Dicey," cried the captain, on hearing this.

"Why such haste?" inquired Gregory.

"Because such a sudden fall in the barometer is a sure sign of approaching bad weather," answered the captain.

The first man on the shrouds and out upon the main-topsail yard was Sam Baker, whose active movements and hearty manner showed that he had quite recovered his health without the use of physic. He was quickly followed by some of his shipmates, all of whom were picked men—able in body and ready for anything.

In a few minutes sail was reduced. Soon after that clouds began to rise on the horizon and spread over the sky. Before half an hour had passed the breeze came—came far stronger than had been expected—and the order to take in sail had to be repeated.

Baker was first again. He was closely followed by Joe Davis and Jim Croft, both of them sturdy fellows— good specimens of the British seaman. Davy Butts, who came next, was not so good a specimen. He was nearly six feet high, very thin and loosely put together, like a piece of bad furniture. But his bones were big, and he was stronger than he looked. He would not have formed one of such a crew had he not been a good man. The rest of the crew, of whom there were eighteen, not including the officers, were of all shapes, sizes, and complexions.

The sails had scarcely been taken in when the storm burst on the brig in all its fury. The waves rose like mountains and followed after her, as if they were eager to swallow her up. The sky grew dark overhead as the night closed in, the wind shrieked through the rigging, and the rag of canvas that they ventured to hoist seemed about to burst away from the yard. It was an awful night. Such a night as causes even reckless men to feel how helpless they are—how dependent on the arm of God. The gale steadily increased until near midnight, when it blew a perfect hurricane.

"It's a dirty night," observed the captain, to the

second mate, as the latter came on deck to relieve the watch.

"It is, sir," replied Mr. Dicey, as coolly as if he were about to sit down to a good dinner on shore. Mr. Dicey was a remarkably matter-of-fact man. He looked upon a storm as he looked upon a fit of the toothache—a thing that had to be endured, and was not worth making a fuss about.

"It won't last long," said the captain.

"No, sir; it won't," answered Mr. Dicey.

As Mr. Dicey did not seem inclined to say more, the captain went below and flung himself on a locker, having given orders that he should be called if any change for the worse took place in the weather. Soon afterward a tremendous sea rose high over the stern, and part of it fell on the deck with a terrible crash, washing Mr. Dicey into the lee-scuppers, and almost sweeping him overboard. On regaining his feet, and his position beside the wheel, the second mate shook himself and considered whether he ought to call the captain. Having meditated some time, he concluded that the weather was no worse, although it had treated him very roughly, so he did not disturb the captain's repose.

Thus the storm raged all that night. It tossed the *Hope* about like a cork; it well-nigh blew the sails off the masts, and almost blew Mr. Dicey's head off his shoulders! then it stopped as it had begun— suddenly.

Chapter III

IN THE ICE—DANGERS OF ARCTIC VOYAGING.

Next morning the *Hope* was becalmed in the midst of a scene more beautiful than the tongue or the pen of man can describe.

When the sun rose that day, it shone upon what appeared to be a field of glass and a city of crystal. Every trace of the recent storm was gone except a long swell, which caused the brig to roll considerably, but which did not break the surface of the sea.

Ice was to be seen all round as far as the eye could reach. Ice in every form and size imaginable. And the wonderful thing about it was that many of the masses resembled the buildings of a city. There were houses, and churches, and monuments, and spires, and ruins. There were also islands and mountains! Some of the pieces were low and flat, no bigger than a boat; others were tall, with jagged tops; some of the fields, as they are called, were a mile and more in extent, and there were a number of bergs, or ice-mountains, higher than the brig's topmasts. These last were almost white, but they had, in many places, a greenish-blue colour that was soft and beautiful. The whole scene shone and sparkled so brilliantly in the morning sun, that one could almost fancy it was one of the regions of a fairyland!

When young Gregory came on the quarter-deck, no one was there except Jim Croft, a short, thick-set man, with the legs of a dwarf and the shoulders of a giant. He stood at the helm, and although no steering was required, as there was no wind, he kept his hands on the spokes of the wheel, and glanced occasionally at the compass. The first mate, who had the watch on deck, was up at the masthead, observing the state of the ice.

"How glorious!" exclaimed the youth, as he swept

his sparkling eye round the horizon. "Ah, Croft! is not this splendid?"

"So it is, sir," said the seaman, turning the large quid of tobacco that bulged out his left cheek. "It's very beautiful, no doubt, but it's comin' rather thick for my taste."

"How so?" inquired Gregory. "There seems to me plenty of open water to enable us to steer clear of these masses. Besides, as we have no wind, it matters little, I should think, whether we have room to sail or not."

"You've not seed much o' the ice yet, that's plain," said Croft, "else you'd know that the floes are closin' round us, an' we'll soon be fast in the pack, if a breeze don't spring up to help us."

As the reader may not, perhaps, understand the terms used by Arctic voyagers in regard to the ice in its various forms, it may be as well here to explain the meaning of those most commonly used.

When ice is seen floating in small detached pieces and scattered masses, it is called "floe" ice, and men speak of getting among the floes. When these floes close up, so that the whole sea seems to be covered with them, and little water can be seen, it is called "pack" ice. When the pack is squeezed together, so that lumps of it are forced up in the form of rugged mounds, these mounds are called "hummocks." A large mass of flat ice, varying from one mile to many miles in extent, is called a "field," and a mountain of ice is called a "berg."

All the ice here spoken of, except the berg, is sea-ice; formed by the freezing of the ocean in winter. The berg is formed in a very different manner. Of this more shall be said in a future chapter.

"Well, my lad," said Gregory, in reply to Jim Croft's last observation, "I have not seen much of the ice yet, as you truly remark, so I hope that the wind will not come to help us out of it for some time. You don't think it dangerous to get into the pack, do you?"

"Well, not exactly dangerous, sir," replied Croft, "but I must say that it aint safe, 'specially when there's a swell on like this. But that'll go down soon. D'ye know what a nip is, Dr. Gregory?"

"I think I do; at least I have read of such a thing. But I should be very glad to hear what you have to say about it. No doubt you have felt one."

"Felt one!" cried Jim, screwing up his face and

drawing his limbs together, as if he were suffering horrible pain, "no, I've never felt one. The man what *feels* a nip aint likely to live to tell what his feelin's was. But I've *seed* one."

"You've seen one, have you? That must have been interesting. Where was it?"

"Not very far from the Greenland coast," said Croft, giving his quid another turn. "This was the way of it. You must know that there was two ships of us in company at the time. Whalers we was. We got into the heart of the pack somehow, and we thought we'd never get out of it again. There was nothin' but ice all round us as far as the eye could see. The name of our ship was the *Nancy*. Our comrade was the *Bullfinch*. One mornin' early we heard a loud noise of ice rubbin' agin the sides o' the ship, so we all jumped up, an' on deck as fast as we could, for there's short time given to save ourselves in them seas sometimes. The whole pack, we found, was in motion, and a wide lead of water opened up before us, for all the world like a smooth river or canal windin' through the pack. Into this we warped the ship, and hoistin' sail, steered away cheerily. We passed close to the *Bullfinch*, which was still hard and fast in the pack, and we saw that her crew were sawin' and cuttin' away at the ice, tryin' to get into the lead that we'd got into. So we hailed them, and said we would wait for 'em outside the pack, if we got through. But the words were no sooner spoken, when the wind it died away, and we were becalmed about half a mile from the *Bullfinch*.

"'You'd better go down to breakfast, boys,' says our captain, says he, 'the breeze won't be long o' comin' again.'

"So down the men went, and soon after that the steward comes on deck, and, says he to the captain, 'Breakfast, sir.' 'Very good,' says the captain, and down he went too, leavin' me at the wheel and the mate in charge of the deck. He'd not been gone three minutes when I noticed that the great field of ice on our right was closin' in on the field on our left, and the channel we was floatin' in was closin' up. The mate noticed it, too, but he wouldn't call the captain 'cause the ice came so slowly and quietly on that for a few minutes we could hardly believe it was movin' and everything around us looked so calm and peaceful like that it was difficult to believe our danger was so great. But this was only a momentary feelin', d'ye see. A minute after that the mate he cries down to the captain—

"'Ice closin' up, sir!'

"And the captain he runs on deck. By this time there was no mistake about it; the ice was close upon us. It was clear that we were to have a nip. So the captain roars down the hatchway, 'Tumble up there! tumble up! every man alive! for your lives!' And sure enough they did tumble up, as I never seed 'em do it before—two or three of 'em was sick; they came up with their clothes in their hands. The ice was now almost touchin' our sides, and I tell *you*, sir, I never did feel so queerish in all my life before as when I looked over the side at the edge of that great field of ice which rose three foot out o' the water, and was, I suppose, six foot more below the surface. It came on so slow that we could hardly see the motion. Inch by inch the water narrowed between it and our sides. At last it touched on the left side, and that shoved us quicker on to the field on our right. Every eye was fixed on it—every man held his breath. You might have heard a pin fall on the deck. It touched gently at first, then there was a low grindin' and crunchin' sound. The ship trembled as if it had been a livin' creetur, and the beams began to crack. Now, you must know, sir, that when a nip o' this sort takes a ship the ice usually eases off, after giving her a good squeeze, or when the pressure is too much for her, the ice slips under her bottom and lifts her right out o' the water. But our *Nancy* was what we call wall-sided. She was never fit to sail in them seas. The consequence was that the ice crushed her sides in. The moment the captain heard the beams begin to go he knew it was all up with the ship; so he roared to take to the ice for our lives! You may be sure we took his advice. Over the side we went, every man Jack of us, and got on the ice. We did not take time to save an article belongin' to us; and it was as well we did not, for the ice closed up with a crash, and we heard the beams and timbers rending like a fire of musketry in the hold. Her bottom must have been cut clean away, for she stood on the ice just as she had floated on the sea. Then the noise stopped, the ice eased off, and the ship began to settle. The lead of water opened up again; in ten minutes after that the *Nancy* went to the bottom and left us standing there on the ice.

"It was the mercy of God that let it happen so near

the *Bullfinch*. We might have been out o' sight o' that ship at the time, and then every man of us would have bin lost. As it was, we had a hard scramble over a good deal of loose ice, jumpin' from lump to lump, and some of us fallin' into the water several times, before we got aboard. Now that was a bad nip, sir, warn't it?"

"It certainly was," replied Gregory; "and although I delight in being among the ice, I sincerely hope that our tight little brig may not be tried in the same way. But she is better able to stand it, I should think."

"That she is, sir," replied Croft, with much confidence. "I seed her in dock, sir, when they was a-puttin' of extra timbers on the bow, and I do believe she would stand twice as much bad usage as the *Nancy* got, though she is only half the size."

Jim Croft's opinion on this point was well founded, for the *Hope* had indeed been strengthened and prepared for her ice battles with the greatest care, by men of experience and ability. As some readers may be interested in this subject, I shall give a brief account of the additions that were made to her hull.

The vessel was nearly two hundred tons burden. She had originally been built very strongly, and might

even have ventured on a voyage to the Polar seas just
as she was. But Captain Harvey resolved to take every
precaution to insure the success of his voyage, and
the safety and comfort of his men. He, therefore, had
the whole of the ship's bottom sheathed with thick
hardwood planking, which was carried up above her
water-line, as high as the ordinary floe-ice would be
likely to reach. The hull inside was strengthened
with stout cross-beams, as well as with beams running
along the length of the vessel, and in every part that
was likely to be subjected to pressure iron stanchions
were fastened. But the bow of the vessel was the point
where the utmost strength was aimed at. Inside, just
behind the cutwater, the whole space was so traversed
by cross-beams of oak that it almost became a solid
mass, and outside the sharp stem was cased in iron
so as to resemble a giant's chisel. The false keel was
taken off, the whole vessel, in short, was rendered as
strong, outside and in, as wood and iron and skill could
make her. It need scarcely be said that all the other
arrangements about her were made with the greatest
care and without regard to expense, for although the
owners of the brig did not wish to waste their money,

they set too high a value on human life to risk it for the sake of saving a few pounds. She was provisioned for a cruise of two years and a half. But this was in case of accidents, for Captain Harvey did not intend to be absent much longer than one year.

But, to return to our story:

Jim Croft's fear that they would be set fast was realised sooner than he expected. The floes began to close in, from no cause that could be seen, for the wind was quite still, and in a short time the loose ice pressed against the *Hope* on all sides. It seemed to young Gregory as if the story that the seaman had just related was about to be enacted over again; and, being a stranger to ice, he could not help feeling a little uneasy for some time. But there was in reality little or no danger, for the pressure was light, and the brig had got into a small bay in the edge of an ice-field, which lay in the midst of the smaller masses.

Seeing that there was little prospect of the pack opening up just then, the captain ordered the ice-anchors to be got out and fixed.

The appearance of the sea from the brig's deck was now extremely wintry, but very bright and cheerful.

Not a spot of blue water was to be seen in any direction. The whole ocean appeared as if it had been frozen over.

It was now past noon, and the sun's rays were warm, although the quantity of ice around rendered the air cold. As the men were returning from fixing the anchors, the captain looked over the side, and said:

"It's not likely that we shall move out of this for some hours. What say you, lads, to a game of football?"

The proposal was received with a loud cheer. The ball had been prepared by the sail-maker, in expectation of some such opportunity as this. It was at once tossed over the side; those men who were not already on the field scrambled out of the brig, and the entire crew went leaping and yelling over the ice with the wild delight of schoolboys let loose for an unexpected holiday.

They were in the middle of the game when a loud shout came from the brig, and the captain's voice was heard singing out:

"All hands ahoy! come aboard. Look alive!"

Instantly the men turned, and there was a general race toward the brig, which lay nearly a quarter of a mile distant from them.

In summer, changes in the motions of the ice take place in the most unexpected manner. Currents in the ocean are, no doubt, the chief cause of these; the action of winds has also something to do with them. One of these changes was now taking place. Almost before the men got on board the ice had separated, and long canals of water were seen opening up here and there. Soon after that a light breeze sprang up, the ice-anchors were taken aboard, the sails trimmed, and soon the *Hope* was again making her way slowly but steadily to the north.

Chapter IV

For some hours the brig proceeded onward with a freshening breeze, winding and turning in order to avoid the lumps of ice. Many of the smaller pieces were not worth turning out of the way of, the mere weight of the vessel being sufficient to push them aside.

Up to this time they had succeeded in steering clear of everything without getting a thump; but they got one at last, which astonished those among the crew who had not been in the ice before. The captain, Gregory, and Dicey were seated in the cabin at the time taking tea. Ned Dawkins, the steward, an active little man, was bringing in a tea-pot with a second supply of tea. In his left hand he carried a tray of biscuit. The captain sat at the head of the table, Dicey at the foot, and the doctor at the side.

Suddenly a tremendous shock was felt! The captain's cup of tea leaped away from him and flooded the centre of the table. The doctor's cup was empty; he seized the table with both hands and remained steady; but Dicey's cup happened to be at his lips at the moment, and was quite full. The effect on him was unfortunate. He was thrown violently on his back, and the tea poured over his face and drenched his hair as he lay sprawling on the floor. The steward saved himself by dropping the bread-tray and grasping the handle of the cabin door. So violent was the shock that the ship's bell was set a-ringing.

"Beg pardon, gentlemen," cried the first mate, looking down the skylight. "I forgot to warn you. The ice is getting rather thick around us, and I had to charge a lump of it."

"It's all very well to beg pardon," said the captain, "but that won't mend my crockery!"

"Or dry my head," growled Mr. Dicey; "it's as bad as if I'd been dipped overboard, it is."

Before Mr. Dicey's grumbling remarks were finished all three of them had reached the deck. The wind had freshened considerably, and the brig was rushing in a somewhat alarming manner among the floes. It required the most careful attention to prevent her striking heavily.

"If it goes on like this, we shall have to reduce sail," observed the captain. "See, there is a neck of ice ahead that will stop us."

This seemed to be probable, for the lane of water along which they were steering was, just ahead of them, stopped by a neck of ice that connected two floe-pieces. The water beyond was pretty free from ice, but this neck or mass seemed so thick that it became a question whether they should venture to charge it or shorten sail.

"Stand by the fore- and main-topsail braces!" shouted the captain.

"Aye, aye, sir!"

"Now, Mr. Mansell," said he, with a smile, "we have come to our first real difficulty. What do you advise;

shall we back the topsails, or try what our little *Hope* is made of, and charge the enemy?"

"Charge!" answered the mate.

"Just so," said the captain, hastening to the bow to direct the steersman. "Port your helm."

"Steady."

The brig was now about fifty yards from the neck of ice, tearing through the water like a race-horse. In another moment she was up to it and struck it fair in the middle. The stout little vessel quivered to her keel under the shock, but she did not recoil. She split the mass into fragments, and, bearing down all before her, sailed like a conqueror into the clear water beyond.

"Well done the *Hope*!" said the captain, as he walked aft, while a cheer burst from the men.

"I think she ought to be called the *Good Hope* ever after this," said Tom Gregory. "If she cuts her way through everything as easily as she has cut through that neck of ice, we shall reach the North Pole itself before winter."

"If we reach the North Pole *at all*," observed Mr. Dicey, "I'll climb up to the top of it and stand on my head, I will!"

The second mate evidently had no expectation of reaching that mysterious pole, which men have so long and so often tried to find, in vain.

"Heavy ice ahead, sir," shouted Mr. Mansell, who was at the masthead with a telescope.

"Where away?"

"On the weather bow, sir, the pack seems open enough to push through, but the large bergs are numerous."

The *Hope* was now indeed getting into the heart of those icy regions where ships are in constant danger from the floating masses that come down with the ocean-currents from the far north. In sailing along she was often obliged to run with great violence against lumps so large that they caused her whole frame to tremble, stout though it was. "Shall we smash the lump, or will it stave in our bows?" was a question that frequently ran in the captain's mind. Sometimes ice closed round her and squeezed the sides so that her beams cracked. At other times, when a large field was holding her fast, the smaller pieces would grind and rasp against her as they went past, until the crew fancied the whole of the outer sheathing of planks had been scraped off. Often she had to press close to ice-bergs of great size, and more than once a lump as large as a good-sized house fell off the ice-fields and plunged into the sea close to her side, causing her to rock violently on the waves that were raised by it.

Indeed the bergs are dangerous neighbours, not only from this cause, but also on account of their turning upside down at times, and even falling to pieces, so that Captain Harvey always kept well out of their way when he could; but this was not always possible. The little brig had a narrow escape one day from the falling of a berg.

It was a short time after that day on which they had the game of football. They passed in safety through the floes and bergs that had been seen that evening, and got into open water beyond, where they made good progress before falling in with ice; but at last they came to a part of Baffin's Bay where a great deal of ice is always found. Here the pack surrounded them, and compelled them to pass close to a berg which was the largest they had fallen in with up to that time. It was jagged in form, and high rather than broad. Great peaks rose up from it like the mountain tops of some wild highland region. It was several hundred yards off the weather-beam when the brig passed, but it towered so high over the masts that it seemed to be much nearer than it was. There was no apparent motion in this berg, and the waves beat and rolled upon its base just as they do on the shore of an island. In fact it was as like an island as possible, or, rather, like a mountain planted in the sea, only it was white instead of green. There were cracks and rents and caverns in it, just as there are on a rugged mountain side, all of which were of a beautiful blue colour. There were also slopes and crags and precipices, down which the water of the melted ice constantly flowed in wild torrents. Many of these were equal to small rivulets, and some of the waterfalls were beautiful. The berg could not have measured less than a mile round the base, and it was probably two hundred feet high. It is well known that floating ice sinks deep, and that there is about eight or ten times as much of it below as there is above water. The reader may therefore form some idea of what an enormous mass of ice this berg was.

The crew of the *Hope* observed, in passing, that

lumps were continually falling from the cliffs into the sea. The berg was evidently in a very rotten and dangerous state, and the captain ran the brig as close to the pack on the other side as possible, in order to keep out of its way. Just as this was done, some great rents occurred, and suddenly a mass of ice larger than the brig fell from the top of a cliff into the sea. No danger flowed from this, but the mass thus thrown off was so large as to destroy the balance of the berg, and, to the horror of the sailors, the huge mountain began to roll over. Fortunately it fell in a direction away from the brig. Had it rolled toward her, no human power could have saved our voyagers. The mighty mass went over with a wild hollow roar, and new peaks and cliffs rose out of the sea, as the old ones disappeared, with great cataracts of uplifted brine pouring furiously down their sides.

Apart from its danger, this was an awful sight. Those who witnessed it could only gaze in solemn silence. Even the most careless among them must have been forced to recognise the might and majesty of God in the event, as well as His mercy in having led them to the *right* side of the berg at such a dangerous moment.

But the scene had not yet closed. For some time the ice mountain rocked grandly to and fro, raising a considerable swell on the sea, which, all round, was covered with the foam caused by this tremendous commotion. In a few minutes several rents took place, sounding like the reports of great guns. Rotten as it was, the berg could not stand the shock of its change of position, for it had turned fairly upside down. Crack after crack took place, with deafening reports. Lumps of all sizes fell from its sides. Then there was a roar, long continued like thunder; a moment after, the whole berg sank down in ruins, and, with a mighty crash, fell flat upon the sea!

The *Hope* was beyond the reach of danger, but she rose and sank on the swell, caused by the ruin of this berg, for some time after.

It was on the afternoon of the same day that the brig received her first really severe "nip" from the ice.

She had got deep into the pack, and was surrounded on all sides by large bergs, some of these being high, like the one that has just been described, others low and flat but of great extent. One, not far off, was two miles long, and its glittering walls rose about fifteen

feet above the sea. The sky was brighter than usual
at the time. This was owing to one of those strange
appearances which one sees more of in the Arctic
regions than in any other part of the world. The sun
shone with unclouded splendour, and around it there
were three mock suns almost as bright as the sun itself,
one on each side and one directly above it. Learned
men call these bright spots *parhelia.* Sailors call them
sun-dogs. They were connected together with a ring
of light which entirely encircled the sun, but the lower
edge of it was partly lost on the horizon.

Although this was the first time that these mock
suns had been seen by Gregory and some others of
the crew of the *Hope*, little attention was paid to them
at the time, because of the dangerous position into
which the brig had been forced. The pack had again
closed all around her, obliging her to take shelter in
the lee of a small berg, which, from its shape, did not
seem likely to be a dangerous protector.

There was a small bay in the berg. Into this the brig
was warped, and for some time she lay safely here. It
was just large enough to hold her, and a long tongue
of ice, projecting from the foot of it, kept off the

pressure of the sea-ice. Nevertheless a look of anxiety rested on the captain's face after the ice-anchors had been made fast.

"You don't seem to like our position, captain," said young Gregory, who had been watching the doings of the men and now and then lent them a hand.

"I don't, Tom. The pack is closing tight up, and this berg may prove an enemy instead of a friend, if it forces into our harbour here. Let us hear what our mate thinks of it. What say you, Mr. Mansell, shall we hold on here, or warp out and take our chance in the pack?"

"Better hold on, sir," answered the mate gravely. "The pack is beginning to grind; we should get a tight embrace, I fear, if we went out. Here we may do well enough; but everything depends on that tongue."

He looked as he spoke toward the point of ice which extended in front of the brig's stern, and guarded the harbour from the outer ice in that direction. The tongue was not a large one, and it was doubtful whether it could stand the pressure that was increasing every minute.

The pack was indeed beginning to "grind," as the

mate had said, for, while they were looking at it, the edges of two floes came together with a crash about fifty yards from the berg. They ground together for a moment with a harsh growling sound, and then the two edges were suddenly forced up to a height of about fifteen or twenty feet. Next moment they fell on the closed-up ice, and lay there in a mound, or *hummock*, of broken masses.

"That's how a 'ummuck is formed, Dr. Gregory," said Mr. Dicey, looking uncommonly wise. "You'll see more things here in five minutes, by means of your own eyes, than ye could learn from books in a year. There's nothin' like seein'. Seein' is believin', you know. I wouldn't give an ounce of experience for a ton of hearsay."

"Come, Mr. Dicey, don't run down book-learning," said Gregory. "If a man only knew about things that he had seen, he would know very little."

Before the second mate could reply the captain shouted to the men to "Bear a hand with the ice-poles." The whole crew answered to the call, and each man, seizing a long pole, stood ready for action.

The tongue to which I have referred more than once

had broken off, and the ice was rushing in. The bay was full in a minute, and although the men used their ice-poles actively, and worked with a will, they could not shove the pieces past them. The *Hope* was driven bow on to the berg. Then there was a strain, a terrible creaking and groaning of the timbers, as if the good little vessel were complaining of the pressure. All at once there was a loud crack, the bow of the brig lifted a little, and she was forced violently up the sloping side of the berg. Twice this happened, and then she remained stationary—high and dry out of the water!

Chapter V

During the rest of that day and the whole of that night did the brig remain fixed on the berg. Early next morning the ice began to move. It eased off, and the vessel slid gently down the slope on which she had been forced, and was re-launched safely into the water.

The satisfaction of the crew, on being thus delivered from a position of much danger, was very great; but they had no sooner escaped from one peril than they were overtaken by another. A sharp breeze sprang up from the eastward, and drove them out into the pack, which began to heave about in a terrible manner under the influence of the wind. Soon this increased to a gale, and the ice was driven along at great speed by a strong northerly current.

While this was going on, land was discovered bearing to the northeast. Here was new danger, for although it was not a lee-shore, still there was some risk of the vessel being caught among grounded icebergs—of which a few were seen.

The gale increased to such a degree before night that Captain Harvey began to think of taking shelter under the lee of one of these bergs. He therefore stood toward one, but before reaching it the vessel received one or two severe shocks from passing floes. A large berg lay within half a mile of them. They reached it in safety, and getting under its lee, lowered a boat and fixed their ice-anchors. Just after they were fixed, a mass of ice, the size of a ship's long-boat and many tons in weight, came suddenly up out of the sea with great violence, the top of it rising above the bulwarks. One corner of it struck the hull just behind the mainmast, and nearly stove in the bottom of the brig.

This lump was what Arctic voyagers term a "calf."

When masses of ice break off from the bergs far below the surface of the water, they rise with extreme violence, and ships run great risk of being destroyed by these calves when they anchor too near to the bergs. Had this calf struck the *Hope* a fair blow she must certainly have gone down with all on board.

They were not yet freed from their troubles, however. In half an hour the wind shifted a few points, but the stream of the loose ice did not change. The brig was, therefore, blown right in among the rushing masses. The three cables that held her were snapped as if they had been pieces of packthread, and she was whirled out into the pack, where she drove helplessly, exposed to the fury of the howling storm and the dangers of the grinding ice. Captain Harvey now felt that he could do nothing to save his vessel. He believed that if God did not mercifully put forth His hand to deliver them by a miracle, he and his companions would certainly perish. In this the captain was wrong. Nothing is impossible to the Almighty. He can always accomplish his purposes without the aid of a miracle.

There did, indeed, seem no way of escape; for the

driving masses of ice were grinding each other to powder in nearly every direction, and the brig only escaped instant destruction by being wedged between two pieces that held together from some unknown cause. Presently they were carried down toward a large berg that seemed to be aground, for the loose ice was passing it swiftly. This was not the case, however. An undercurrent, far down in the depths of the sea, was acting on this berg, and preventing it from travelling with the ice that floated with the stream at the surface. In its passing, the mass of ice that held them struck one of the projecting tongues beneath the surface, and was split in two. The brig was at once set free. As they passed they might almost have leaped upon the berg. Captain Harvey saw and seized his opportunity.

"Stand by to heave an anchor," he shouted.

Sam Baker, being the strongest man in the ship, sprang to one of the small ice-anchors that lay on the deck with a line attached to it, and, lifting it with both hands, stood ready.

The brig passed close to the end of the berg, where the lee-side formed a long tail of sheltered water. She was almost thrust into this by the piece of ice from which she had just escaped. She grazed the edge of the berg as she drove past.

"Heave!" shouted the captain.

Sam Baker swung the anchor round his head as if it had been a feather, and hurled it far upon the ice. For a few yards it rattled over the slippery surface; then it caught a lump, but the first strain broke it off. Just after that it fell into a crack and held on. The brig was checked, and swung round into the smooth water; but they had to ease off the line lest it should snap. At last she was brought up, and lay safely under the shelter of that berg until the storm was over.

Some weeks flew by after this without anything occurring worthy of particular notice. During this time the *Hope* made good progress into the Polar regions, without again suffering severely either from ice or storm, although much retarded by the thick fogs that prevail in the Arctic regions. She was indeed almost always surrounded by ice, but it was sufficiently open to allow of a free passage through it. Many whales and seals had been seen, also one or two bears, but not in circumstances in which they could be attacked without occasioning much delay.

The brief summer had now passed away, and the days began to shorten as winter approached. Still Captain Harvey hoped to get farther north before being obliged to search for winter quarters. One morning early in September, however, he found to his sorrow that pancake-ice was forming on the sea. When the sea begins to freeze it does so in small needle-like spikes, which cross and recross each other until they form thin ice, which the motion of the waves breaks up into flat cakes about a foot or so across. These, by constantly rubbing against each other, get worn into a rounded shape. Sailors call this "pancake-ice." It is the first sign of coming winter. The cakes soon become joined together as the frost increases.

The place where this occurred was near to those wild cliffs that rise out of the sea in the channels or straits that lie at the head of Baffin's Bay. The vessel was now beyond the farthest point of land that had been discovered at the time of which I am writing, and already one or two of the headlands had been named by Captain Harvey and marked on his chart.

"I don't like to see pancake-ice so early in the

season," remarked the captain to Mr. Mansell.

"No more do I, sir," answered the mate. "This would be a bad place to winter in, I fear."

"Land ahead!" was shouted at that moment by the look-out at the masthead.

"Keep her away two points," said the captain to the man at the helm. "How does it lie?"

"Right ahead, sir."

"Any ice near it?"

"No; all clear."

The brig was kept a little more out to sea. Soon she came to more open water, and in the course of four hours was close to the land, which proved to be a low, barren island, not more than a mile across.

Here the wind died away altogether, and a sharp frost set in. The pancakes became joined together, and on the following morning, when our friend Gregory came on deck, he found that the whole ocean was covered with ice! It did not, indeed, look very like ice, because, being so thin, it did not prevent the usual swell from rolling over the sea. A light breeze was blowing, and the brig cut her way through it for some time; but the breeze soon died away, leaving her becalmed within a quarter of a mile of the island.

For some time the voyagers hoped that a thaw would take place, or that wind would break up the ice. But they were disappointed. This was the first touch of the cold hand of winter, and the last day of the Hope's advance northward.

Seeing this, Captain Harvey set energetically to work to cut his way into winter quarters, for it would not do to remain all winter in the exposed position in which his vessel then lay. On his right was the island, already referred to, about a quarter of a mile off. Beyond this, about five miles distant, were the high steep cliffs of the western coast of Greenland. Everywhere else lay the open sea, covered here and there with floes and bergs, and coated with new ice.

This ice became so thick in the course of another night that the men could walk on it without danger. By means of saws and chisels made for the purpose, they cut a passage toward the island, and finally moored the brig in a small bay which was sheltered on all sides except the east. This, being the land side, required no protection. They named the place "Refuge Harbour."

Everyone was now full of activity. The voyagers had

reached the spot where they knew they were destined to spend the winter and much had to be done before they could consider themselves in a fit state to face that terrible season.

Winter in the Polar regions extends over eight months of the year—from September to May. But so much of ice and snow remains there all the summer that winter can scarcely be said to quit those regions at all.

It is difficult to imagine what the Arctic winter is. We cannot properly understand the tremendous difficulties and sufferings that men who go to the Polar seas have to fight against. Let the reader think of the following facts, and see if he does not draw his chair closer to the fire and feel thankful that he has not been born an Eskimo, and is not an Arctic seaman!

Winter within the Arctic circle, as I have said, is fully eight months long. During that time the land is covered with snow many feet deep, and the sea with ice of all degrees of thickness—from vast fields of ten or fifteen feet thick to bergs the size of islands and mountains—all frozen into one solid mass.

There is no sunlight there, night or day, for three

out of these eight winter months, and there is not much during the remaining five. In summer there is perpetual sunlight, all night as well as all day, for about two months—for many weeks the sun never descends below the horizon. It is seen every day and every night sweeping a complete circle in the bright blue sky. Having been so free of his light in summer, the sun seems to think he has a right to absent himself in winter, for the three months of darkness that I have spoken of are not months of *partial* but of *total* darkness—as far, at least, as the sun is concerned. The moon and stars and the "Northern Lights" do, indeed, give their light when the fogs and clouds will allow them; but no one will say that these make up for the absence of the sun.

Then the frost is so intense that everything freezes solid except pure spirits of wine. Unless you have studied the thermometer you cannot understand the intensity of this frost; but for the sake of those who do know something about extreme cold, I give here a few facts that were noted down during the winter that my story tells of.

On the 10th of September these ice-bound voyagers

had eighteen degrees of frost, and the darkness had advanced on them so rapidly that it was dark about ten at night. By the 1st of October the ice round the brig was a foot and a half thick. Up to this time they had shot white hares on the island, and the hunting parties that crossed the ice to the mainland shot deer and musk oxen, and caught white foxes in traps. Gulls and other birds, too, had continued to fly around them; but most of these went away to seek warmer regions farther south. Walrus and seals did not leave so soon. They remained as long as there was any open water out at sea. The last birds that left them, (and the first that returned in spring) were the "snow-birds"— little creatures about the size of a sparrow, almost white, with a few brown feathers here and there. The last of these fled from the darkening winter on the 7th of November, and did not return until the 1st of the following May. When they left it was dark almost all day. The thermometer could scarcely be read at noon, and the stars were visible during the day. From this time forward thick darkness set in, and the cold became intense. The thermometer fell *below* zero, and after that they never saw it *above* that point for months together—20 degrees, 30 degrees, and 40 degrees below were common temperatures. The ice around them was ten feet thick. On the 1st of December noon was so dark that they could not see fifty yards ahead, and on the 15th the fingers could not be counted a foot from the eyes. The thermometer stood at 40 degrees below zero.

The darkness could not now become greater, but the cold still continued to grow more intense. It almost doubled in severity. In January it fell to 67 degrees below zero! So great was this cold that the men felt impelled to breathe gradually. The breath issued from their mouths in white clouds of steam and instantly settled on their beards and whiskers in hoar-frost. In the cabin of the *Hope* they had the utmost difficulty in keeping themselves moderately warm at this time.

Things had now reached their worst, and by slow degrees matters began to mend. On the 22nd of January the first faint sign of returning day appeared— just a blue glimmer on the horizon. By the middle of February the light tipped the tops of the mountains on shore, and the highest peaks of the ice-bergs on the sea, and on the 1st of March it bathed the deck of the *Hope*. Then the long-imprisoned crew began to feel that spring was really coming. But there was little heat in the sun's rays at first, and it was not till the month of May that the ice out at sea broke up and summer could be said to have begun.

During all this long winter—during all these wonderful changes, our Arctic voyagers had a hard fight in order to keep themselves alive. Their life was a constant struggle. They had to fight the bears and the walrus; to resist the cold and the darkness; to guard against treachery from the natives; and to suffer pains, sickness, and trials, such as seldom fall to the lot of men in ordinary climates.

How they did and suffered all this I shall try to show in the following pages. In attempting this I shall make occasional extracts from the journal of our friend Tom Gregory, for Tom kept his journal regularly, and was careful to note down only what he heard and saw.

Chapter VI

The first care of Captain Harvey, after getting his brig securely laid up in her icy cradle for the winter was to remove some of the stores to the island, where he had them carefully secured in a little hut which the crew built of loose stones. This relieved the strain on the vessel, and permitted the free circulation of air. The fitting up of the interior of the brig was then begun.

The wooden partition between the cabin and the hold was taken down, and the whole space thrown into one apartment. The stove was put up in the centre of it, and moss was piled round the walls inside about a foot thick. Moss was also spread on the deck, and above it the snow was allowed to gather, for snow, although so cold itself, keeps things that it covers warm, by not permitting the heat to escape. The brig was banked up all round with snow, and a regular snowy staircase was built from the ice to her bulwarks.

They changed their time, now, from what is called sea-time to that which we follow on land. That is to say, they reckoned the day to commence just after twelve, midnight, instead of dividing it into watches, as they were wont to do at sea. Journals were begun, and careful notes made of everything that occurred, or that might in any way further the object for which they had gone there. Every man in the ship had his appointed duty and his post. If the native Eskimos should arrive in a warlike temper, each man had his cutlass and pistols in readiness. If a bear should pay them a visit, each could lay hands on his musket in an instant; and if a fire should break out on board, every man had his bucket ready and his particular post fixed. Some were to run to the water-hole, which it was the duty of one man to keep open. Others were to station themselves from the hole to the ship to pass the buckets, while the rest were to remain on board to convey them to the point of danger. Captain Harvey fixed all the arrangements, and superintended the carrying out of his orders in a general way, making his two officers and the young doctor responsible for the overseeing of details. Each of these foremen furnished him with a report every night of what had been done during the day, and the result was noted down by himself in a journal. Thus everything went smoothly and pleasantly along during the first weeks of their sojourn in their frozen home.

In regard to fresh provisions they were fortunate at first, for they obtained sufficient supplies of deer and other game. This was in the early part of winter, while there was still plenty of daylight. In Tom Gregory's journal I find it thus written:

"*September 10th.*—The days are beginning to shorten now, and we are all busily occupied in preparing for the long, dark winter that is before us. Sam Baker, who is the best shot among us, brought in a deer to-day. This is fortunate, for we stand in need of fresh meat. Our greatest enemy this winter, I fear, will be scurvy.

Unless we obtain a large supply of fresh provisions we cannot hope to escape it. Crofts brought in two Arctic hares. They are beautiful creatures—pure white—and each weighs about seven pounds. These, with the four deer shot by myself last week and the ten hares got by Baker, will keep us going for some time.

"*September 12th.*—I had an adventure with a polar bear last night, which has amused the men very much, and given them food for jocularity for a few days. Some days back Davy Butts set a trap on the island, in which he has caught a few foxes. Last night his long legs were so tired that he did not care to visit his trap, so I offered to go instead of him. It was while I was out on this errand that I happened to meet with bruin. Our meeting was sudden and unexpected on both sides, I believe. It was midnight when I set off to the trap, which was not more than half a mile from the ship, and it was quite dark when I reached it.

"Davy is an ingenious fellow. His trap is made of four blocks of hard snow, with a sort of wooden trigger that goes off the moment the bait is touched, and allows a heavy log to fall down on the poor fox's back. There was no fox there, however, when I reached it. I went down on my knees and was examining the bait, when I heard a low growl. I leaped up, and felt for the knife which I usually carried in my belt. It was not there! In the haste of my departure from the ship I had forgotten to buckle it on. I had no gun, of course. It was too dark to shoot, and I had not counted on meeting with any dangerous enemy. I could only crouch down behind a lump of ice and hope that the bear would go away, but another growl, much louder than the first, and close at hand, showed that I had been seen. It was so dark that I could hardly see fifty yards ahead. There was a great chasm or hole just in front of me. This was the place where the main body of the sea-ice had been separated from the shore-ice that was aground. Here every rise and fall of the tide had broken it afresh, so that the rent was twenty yards wide, and full of large blocks that had been tossed about in confusion. Across this I gazed into the gloom, and thought I saw an object that looked like a large block of rounded ice. Before I could make up my mind how to act, the block of ice rose up with a furious roar and charged me. The chasm checked him for a moment. But for this I should have been caught immediately. While he was scrambling over it I took to my heels, and ran along the edge of the ice at the top of my speed.

"There was a narrow part of the chasm which I had looked at in daylight, and wondered whether I might venture to leap across it. I had made up my mind that it was too wide and dangerous to be attempted. But it is wonderful how quickly a man changes his mind on such a point when a polar bear is roaring at his heels. I came to the gap in the ice. It was ten feet deep and thirteen or fourteen feet across. The jagged lumps of ice at the bottom lay there in horrible confusion. There was barely light enough to see where the hole was when I came within ten yards of it, but I did not hesitate. A rush! a bound! and I went over like a cat. Not so the bear. He had not measured the place with his eye in daylight, as I had done. He made a gallant leap, it is true, but fell short, as I knew from the bursting sound and the growl of rage with which he came against the edge of the ice, and fell back among the broken blocks. I did not wait to see how he got out, you may be sure, but ran as I never ran before in all my life! I reached the brig quite out of breath. The bear had not followed me up, for I did not see him that night again. Long Davy laughed at me a good deal, and said he was sure I had been frightened at a shadow. It gave a wonderfully loud roar for a shadow! I hope that Davy himself may get a chase before the winter is over, just to convince him of his error in not believing me!"

The kind wish thus expressed in the young doctor's journal was gratified sooner than might have been expected.

Only two days after the incident above described, poor Davy Butts met with the same bear, face to face, and had a run for his life, that turned the laugh from Tom Gregory to himself.

It was on the afternoon of a clear, cold day, just about sunset. The men had finished dinner and were smoking their pipes on deck, stamping their feet and slapping their hands and arms, to keep them warm.

"Hallo, Davy! where are you bound for?" inquired the captain, on observing that Butts was wrapping himself carefully in his fur-coat, tightening his belt, and putting on his mittens as if bent on a long journey.

"I'm only goin' to take a look at my fox-trap, sir, if you'll allow me."

"Certainly, my lad. If you get a fox it's well worth the trouble. And hark'ee, Davy, take your axe and make one or two more of these snow-traps of yours. It will be a well-spent hour."

"Why, Butts," exclaimed Gregory, "what do you mean to do with that big horse-pistol? Surely you are not afraid of bears after laughing so much at the one that chased me?"

"Oh, no, not *afraid*, you know," replied Davy. "But there's no harm in being armed."

"Mind you shoot him straight in the eye, or send a bullet up his nose. Them's the vulnerable parts of him," cried Joe Davis, with a laugh, as Butts went down the snow-steps and got upon the ice.

"I say," cried Pepper, as he was moving away.

"Well?"

"Bring his tongue aboard with you, and I'll cook it for supper."

"Ah, and a bit of fat to fry it in," added the steward. "There's nothin' like tongue fried in bear's grease."

"No, no, Dawkins," said Mr. Dicey. "Hallo! Davy; bring the 'ams. Bear's 'ams are considered fustrate heatin'."

"No, *don't* bring the hams," shouted Jim Croft, "fetch the tongue; that's the thing for supper of a cold night—fetch the tongue, lad."

"Hold your own tongue," shouted Davy, in reply, as he went off amid the laughter of his comrades.

The sun sank soon after, and before the ingenious seaman had finished two new traps the short twilight had gradually deepened into night. Still there was plenty of light, for the sky was clear, and studded with a host of stars. In addition to this the Aurora Borealis was sending its beautiful flashes of pale-green light all across the western sky.

The Aurora—which also goes by the names of "Northern Lights," and "Streamers," and "Merry-dancers," is seen in great splendour in these northern skies. When the seaman had finished his traps, and looked up for a minute or two at the sky, before starting on his return to the ship, he beheld the Aurora extending over the heavens in the form of an irregular arch. It was extremely bright, but the brightness was not the same in all parts. It moved and waved gently about like a band of thin green fire. Every now and then long tongues or streamers darted up from it, and these were brighter than the rest. They were yellowish white, and sometimes became pale pink in colour. The light from this beautiful object was equal to that of the moon in her quarter, and the stars that were behind it shone dimly through, as if they were covered with a thin gauze veil.

While Davy was gazing in wonder at the splendid lights above him, a deep growl fell upon his ear. If the man had been a Jack-in-the-box he could not have leaped more quickly round. His pistol was out and cocked in a moment!

The growl was followed by a roar, which drove all the blood back into Davy's heart, and seemed to freeze it there—solid.

The man was no coward, as was quite clear, for at first he boldly stood his ground. But he would have been more than mortal if he had not felt some strange qualms about his heart when he saw a large white bear rushing furiously toward him. The animal came this time from the interior of the small island. The seaman knew well the place over which young Gregory had jumped when he had been chased. After wavering for a moment or two he turned and fled. Another tremendous roar helped him over the ice like a deer, and he took the chasm with a bound like an India-rubber ball.

It must certainly have been the same animal that chased Gregory, for, instead of trying to leap the chasm, it went to another part of the rent and scrambled across. This gave Butts time to increase the distance between them, but a man is no match for a polar bear in a race. The monster was soon close up with him, and the ship still far off. The man knew his danger; he turned, took a quick aim, and fired. He missed, of course; flung the pistol in desperation in the bear's face, and ran on. The pistol happened to stick in the snow, with the butt in the air, and when the bear came up to it he stopped to smell it!

It it well known, nowadays, that polar bears are full of curiosity, and will stop for a few minutes to examine anything that comes in their way, even when they are in full chase of a man. Davy Butts knew nothing of this at the time; but he was a quick-witted fellow. He observed this stopping of the bear, and determined to give him something more to stop at.

When bruin was close at his heels he threw down his cap. The bear at once pulled up, smelt it all round, tossed it into the air with his snout, pawed it once or twice, then tore it to pieces with one wrench, and continued the chase. Very little time was lost in this operation. He was soon up with the man again; then a mitten was thrown down for his inspection. After that the other mitten went, the cravat followed, and the axe went next. All that I have just related happened in a very few minutes. Davy was still a good quarter of a mile from the brig; everything that he could tear off his person in haste and throw down was gone, and the bear was once more coming up behind. As a last hope he pulled off his heavy fur-coat and dropped it. This seemed to be a subject of great interest to the bear, for it was longer in inspecting it than the other things. And now poor Butts went tearing along like a maniac, in his flannel shirt and trousers. He was a miserable and curious object, for his body, besides being very long, was uncommonly lanky, and his legs and arms seemed to go like the wings of a windmill. Never, since the day of his birth, had Davy Butts run at such a pace, in such light clothing, and in such severe frost!

A long line of low hummocks hid him from the

brig. The moment he passed these he came in sight of her and began to yell.

"Wot on airth is yon?" exclaimed Joe Davis, who chanced to be looking over the gangway when this remarkable object appeared.

"The wild man o' the North himself, or my name aint Jim," said Crofts, turning pale.

"Why, it's Davy Butts, I do believe," cried Sam Baker, who came on deck at that moment.

Just then the bear came tearing round the end of the hummocks in full chase.

"Hurrah! hallo! ho!" roared the men, who had crowded on deck at the first note of alarm.

Sam Baker seized a heavy ash handspike about five feet long, and was on his way to meet his comrade before the others had gained the ice. They were not slow, however. Some with muskets, some with pistols and cutlasses, and some with nothing but their fists—all followed Sam, who was now far ahead.

Baker passed Davy without a remark, and ran straight at the bear, which stopped on seeing such a big, powerful man running so furiously at him, and flourishing a bludgeon that would almost have suited the hand of a giant. But polar bears are not timid. He rose on his hind legs at once, and paid no attention whatever to the tremendous crack that Sam dealt him over the skull. The blow broke the handspike in two, and the fool-hardy seaman would soon have paid for his rashness with his life had not friendly and steady hands been near. Nothing daunted, he was about to repeat the blow with the piece of the handspike that was still in his grasp, and the bear was about to seize him with its claws, each of which were full two inches long, when the first mate and Gregory came running toward him, side by side, the first armed with a rifle, the doctor with pistols.

"Too late," gasped Gregory.

"We must fire," said Mansell, "and risk hitting Sam. Here, doctor, you are a good shot; take the rifle."

The young man obeyed, dropped on one knee, and took aim, but did not fire. Sam was between him and the bear. A sudden movement changed their positions. The side of the monster came into view, and in another instant it was stretched on the ice with a bullet in his brain.

Chapter VII

A GREAT BATTLE WITH THE WALRUS.

It need scarcely be said that there was a jovial feast that night at supper. The bear's tongue was cooked after all, but the impudent tongues of the party were not silenced, for they almost worried the life out of poor Davy from having run away from a bear.

Soon after this event the preparations for spending the winter were completed; at least as far as the fitting up of the vessel was concerned.

"This morning," writes Gregory, in his journal, "we finished housing over our Arctic home. The *Hope* is very snug, lined with moss, and almost covered with snow. A sail has been spread over the quarter-deck like an awning; it is also covered with moss and snow. This, we hope, will give much additional warmth to our house below. We all live together now, men and officers. It will require our united strength to fight successfully against that terrible enemy, John Frost. John is king of the Arctic regions, undoubtedly!

"Dawkins got a cold-bath yesterday that amused the men much and did him no harm. For some time past we have been carrying moss from the island in large bundles. Dawkins got leave to help, as he said he was sick-tired of always working among stores. He was passing close to the fire-hole with a great bundle of moss on his back, when his foot slipped, and down he went. This hole is kept constantly open. It is Baker's duty night and morning to break the ice and have it ready in case of fire. The ice on the surface was therefore thin; in a moment nothing was to be seen of poor Dawkins but his bundle! Fortunately he held tight on to it, and we hauled him out, soaked to the skin. The thermometer stood at 35 degrees below zero, the coldest day we have had up to this time; and in two minutes the unfortunate man's clothes were frozen so stiff that he could scarcely walk! We had to break the ice on his legs and arms at the joints, and even then he had to be half hoisted on board and carried below. We all dress in seal-skin and fox-skin garments now. Dawkins had on a rough coat, made of white and grey foxes; trousers of the same; boots of seal-skin, and mittens ditto. When all this was soaked and frozen he was truly a humbling sight!

"The undressing of him was a labour of difficulty as well as of love. However, when he was rubbed dry, and re-clothed, he was none the worse. Indeed, I am inclined to think he was much the better of his ducking.

"To-morrow we are to make some curious experiments with boats, sledges, and kites. The captain is anxious to take our largest boat over the ice as far to the south as possible, and leave her there with a quantity of provisions, so that we may have her to fall back upon if any misfortune should befall the brig, which I earnestly pray that God may forbid.

"Davy Butts, who is an ingenious fellow in his way, says that we can sail a boat on the ice almost as well as on the water, and that we may drag sledges by means of kites, if we choose. The captain means to attempt a journey to the north with sledges in spring, so, if the kites answer, Butts will have done us good service. But I have my doubts.

"The nights are closing in fast; very soon we shall be without the sun altogether. But the moon is cheering us. Last night, (28th October) she swept in a complete circle round the sky *all day* as well as all night. She only touched the horizon, and then, instead of setting, she rose again, as if the frozen sea had frightened her.

"*October 30th.*—Baker came in to-day and reported open water about six miles off, and walrus sporting in it. I shall set out to-morrow on a hunt."

The hunt which the young doctor here wrote of came off the following day, but it was a very different one from what any of the men had expected.

Early in the morning, Baker, Davy Butts, and Gregory set off on foot, armed with a rifle and two muskets, besides a couple of harpoons, a whale-lance, and a long line. They also took a small sledge, which was intended to be used in hauling home the meat if they should be successful. Three hours' hard walking brought the party to the edge of the solid ice, after which they travelled on the floes that were being constantly broken by the tides, and were only joined together by ice of a night or two old. This was little more than an inch thick, so they had to advance with caution.

Presently the loud mooing of a bull walrus was heard. Its roar was something between the lowing of a bull and the bark of a large dog, but much louder, for the walrus resembles an elephant in size more than any other animal. Soon after they came in sight of their game. Five walrus were snorting and barking in a hole which they had broken in the ice. The way in which this huge monster opens a hole when he wants to get out of the sea is to come up from below with considerable violence and send his head crashing through the ice.

The three men now became very wary. They crept on their hands and knees behind the ice-hummocks until within about a hundred yards of the brutes. Then they ascended a small hummock to take a look round and decide on their plan of operations. While lying there, flat on their faces, they took particular care to keep their heads well concealed, just raising them high enough to observe the position of the walrus. There was a sheet of flat ice between them and the hole, so that it was impossible to advance nearer without being seen. This perplexed them much, for although their bullets might hit at that distance, they would not be able to run in quick enough to use their lances, and the harpoons would be of no use at all.

While thus undecided what to do, they were unexpectedly taught a lesson in walrus-hunting that surprised them not a little.

"Hallo! there's a bear!" whispered Davy Butts, as a hairy object crawled out from behind an ice-hummock about two hundred yards from the place where they lay, and made toward the walrus in a sly, cat-like manner.

"More like a seal," observed Baker.

"A seal! why, it's a *man!*" said Gregory, in a low, excited whisper.

"So it is, sure enough," said Baker; "it must be an Eskimo, though his hairy garments make him look more like a bear than a man, and as the fellow has got here before us, I suppose we must give up our claim to the brutes."

"Time enough to talk of that when the brutes are killed," said Gregory with a smile. "But lie still, lads. We will take a lesson from this fellow, who has been so earnestly staring at the walrus that he has not noticed us."

The three men lay perfectly motionless watching the native, who crept as near to the hole as he could without being seen, and then waited for a few minutes until the creatures should dive. This they were constantly doing; staying down a few moments at a time, and then coming up to breathe—for the walrus cannot live without air. He is not a fish, and although he can stay down a long time, he *must* come to the surface occasionally to breathe. In this he resembles the seal and the whale.

Presently, down they all went with a tremendous splash. Now was the moment! the Eskimo rose, ran at full speed for a few yards, then fell flat on his face, and lay quite still as if he had been shot dead. The reason of this was soon apparent. He understood the habits of the walrus, and knew that they would rise again. This they did almost the moment after, and began their snorting, bellowing, and rolling again. Once more they dived. Up got the Eskimo, ran a few yards further forward, and then fell flat down as before. In this way he got near to the hole without being seen.

The watchers observed that he carried a harpoon and a coil of thick line.

The next time the walrus dived he ran to the edge of the hole, but now, instead of falling down, he stood quite still with the harpoon raised above his head ready to be thrown. In a few moments the monsters reappeared. Two rose close at the edge of the hole; one was a male, the other a female. They were frightfully ugly to look at. Shaking the water from his head and shoulders, the bull at once caught sight of the man who had thus suddenly appeared. At that instant the Eskimo threw up his left arm. This action, instead of frightening the brutes away, caused them to raise themselves high out of the water, in order to have a good look at the strange creature who had thus dared to disturb them in their watery home. This was just what the native wanted. It gave him a chance of driving the harpoon under the flipper of the male. The instant this was done he caught up the end of his coil and ran quickly back to the full length of the line.

The battle that now begun was perhaps one of the fiercest that was ever fought in the Arctic regions. The walrus lashed the water furiously for a second or two and dived. This checked the native, who at once stopped running, drove the sharp point of a little piece of wood into the ice, and put the loop at the end of his line over it. He pressed the loop close down to the ice with his feet, so that he could hold on when it tightened, which it did with great force. But the line was a stout one. It had been cut from the hide of a walrus, and prepared in a peculiar way for the purpose of standing a heavy strain.

The Eskimo now played the monster as an angler plays a trout. At one moment he held on, the next he eased off. The line was sometimes like a bar of iron, then it was slackened off as the animal rose and darted about. After this had happened once or twice the bull came to the surface, blowing tremendously, and began to bark and roar in great fury. The female came up at the same time. She evidently meant to stick by her partner and share his danger. The others had dived and made off at the first sign of war.

The wounded walrus was a little flurried and very

angry; the female was not at all frightened, she was passionately furious! Both of them tore up the ice tables with their great ivory tusks, and glared at their enemy with an expression that there was no mistaking. The walrus is well known to be one of the fiercest animals in the world. Woe to the poor native if he had been caught by these monsters at that time.

After some minutes spent in uselessly smashing the ice and trying to get at the native, they both dived. Now came into play the Eskimo's knowledge of the animal's habits and his skill in this curious kind of warfare. Before diving they looked steadily at the man for a second, and then swam under the ice straight for the spot where he stood. The Eskimo of course could not see this, but he knew it from past experience. He therefore changed his position instantly; ran a few yards to one side, and planted his stick and loop again. This had hardly been done when the ice burst up with a loud crash; a hole of more than fifteen feet wide was made on the exact spot which the man had quitted, and the walrus appeared with a puff like that of a steam-engine, and a roar that would have done credit to a lion.

THE WALRUS HUNT—PAGE 242

The great lumpish-looking heads and square-cut faces of the creatures looked frightful at this point in the fight. There was something like human intelligence in their malicious and brutal faces, as the water poured down their cheeks and over their bristling beards, mingled with blood and foam.

At this moment there was a shout close at hand, and two other Eskimos ran out from behind the ice-hummocks and joined their comrade. They were armed with long lances, the handles of which were made of bone, and the points of beautiful white ivory tipped with steel. It was afterwards discovered that these natives obtained small pieces of iron and steel from the Eskimos further south, who were in the habit of trading at the settlements on the coast of Greenland.

The strangers at once ran to the edge of the pool and gave the bull walrus two deep wounds with their lances. They also wounded the female. This seemed to render them more furious than ever. They dived again. The first Eskimo again shifted his position, and the others ran back a short distance. They were not a moment too soon in these changes, for the ice was again burst upward at the spot they had just quitted, and the enraged beasts once more came bellowing to the surface and vented their fury on the ice.

It may seem almost incredible to the reader, *but it is a fact*, that this battle lasted fully four hours. At the end of the third hour it seemed to the sailors who were watching it, that the result was still doubtful, for the Eskimos were evidently becoming tired, while the monsters of the Polar seas were still furious.

"I think we might help them with a butlet," whispered Baker. "It might frighten them, perhaps, but it would save them a good deal of trouble."

"Wait a little longer," replied Gregory. "I have it in my mind to astonish them. You see they have wounded the female very badly, but when the male dies, which he cannot now be long of doing, she will dive and make off, and so they'll lose her, for they don't seem to have another harpoon and line."

"Perhaps they have one behind the hummocks," suggested Davy Butts, whose teeth were chattering in his head with cold.

"If they had they would have used it long ago," said Gregory. "At any rate I mean to carry out my plan—

which is this. When the bull is about dead I will fire at the female and try to hit her in a deadly part, so as to kill her at once. Then, Sam, you will run out with our harpoon and dart into her to prevent her sinking, or diving if she should not be killed. And you, Davy, will follow me and be ready with a musket."

This plan had just been settled when the bull walrus began to show signs of approaching death. Gregory therefore took a deliberate aim with the rifle and fired. The result was startling! The female walrus began to roll and lash about furiously, smashing the ice and covering the sea around with bloody foam. At first the Eskimos stood motionless—rooted to the spot, as if they had been thunderstruck. But when they saw Sam Baker dart from behind the hummock, flourishing his harpoon, followed by Gregory and Butts, their courage deserted them; they turned in terror and fled.

On getting behind the hummocks, however, they halted and peeped over the ledges of ice to see what the seamen did.

Sam Baker, being an old whaleman, darted his harpoon cleverly, and held fast the struggling animal. At the same time Davy Butts seized the end of the line which the natives had thrown down in terror, and held on to the bull. It was almost dead, and quite unable to show any more fight. Seeing that all was right, Gregory now laid down his rifle and advanced slowly to the hummock, behind which the Eskimos had taken refuge.

He knew, from the reports of previous travellers, that holding up both arms is a sign of peace with the Eskimos. He therefore stopped when within a short distance of the hummocks and held up his arms. The signal was understood at once. The natives leaped upon the top of the hummock and held up their arms in reply. Again Gregory tossed up his, and made signs to them to draw near. This they did without hesitation, and the doctor shook them by the hand and patted their hairy shoulders. They were all of them stout, well-made fellows, about five feet seven or eight inches high, and very broad across the shoulders. They were fat, too, and oily-faced, jolly-looking men. They smiled and talked to each other for a few moments and then spoke to Gregory, but when he shook his head, as much as to say, "I don't understand you," they burst into a loud laugh. Then they suddenly became grave, and ran at full speed toward the hole where the walrus floated.

Davy Butts made the usual sign of friendship and handed them the end of their line, which they seized, and set about securing their prize without taking any farther notice of their new friends.

The manner in which these wild yet good-natured fellows hauled the enormous carcass out of the water was simple and ingenious. They made four cuts in the neck, about two inches apart from each other, and raised the skin between these cuts, thus making two bands. Through one of these bands they passed a line, and carried it to a stick made fast in the ice, where they passed it through a loop of well-greased hide. It was then carried back to the animal, made to pass under the second band, and the end was hauled in by the Eskimos. This formed a sort of double purchase, that enabled them to pull out of the hole a carcass which double their numbers could not have hauled up.

Some idea of the bull's weight may be formed when I say that the carcass was eighteen feet long and eleven feet in circumference at the thickest part. There were no fewer than sixty deep lance-wounds in various parts of its body.

When seen close at hand the walrus is a very ugly monster. It is something like a gigantic seal, having two large flippers, or fins, near its shoulders, and two others behind, that look like its tail. It uses these in swimming, but can also use them on land, so as to crawl, or rather to bounce forward in a clumsy fashion. By means of its fore-flippers it can raise itself high out of the water, and get upon the ice and rocks. It is fond of doing this, and is often found sleeping in the sunshine on the ice and on rocks. It has even been known to scramble up the side of an island to a height of a hundred feet, and there lie basking in the sun.

Nevertheless, the water is the proper element of the walrus. All its motions are clumsy and slow until it gets into the sea; there it is "at home." Its upper face has a square, bluff look, and its broad muzzle and cheeks are covered by a coarse beard of bristles, like quills. The two white tusks point downward. In this they are unlike to those of the elephant. The tusks of the bull killed on this occasion were thirty inches long. The hide of the walrus is nearly an inch thick, and is covered with close, short hair. Beneath the skin he has a thick layer of fat, and this enables him to resist the extreme cold in the midst of which he dwells.

The walrus is of great value to the Eskimos. But for it and the seal these poor members of the human family could not exist at all in those frozen regions. As it is, it costs them a severe struggle to keep the life in their bodies. But they do not complain of what seems to us a hard lot. They have been born to it. They know no happier condition of life. They wish for no better home, and the All-wise Creator has fitted them admirably, both in mind and body, to live and even to enjoy life in a region where most other men could live only in great discomfort, if they could exist at all.

The Eskimos cut the walrus' thick hide into long lines with which they hunt—as we have seen. They do not cut these lines in strips and join them in many places; but, beginning at one end of the skin, they cut round and round without break to the centre, and thus secure a line of many fathoms in length.

It is truly said that "necessity is the mother of invention." These natives have no wood. Not a single tree grows in the whole land of which I am writing. There are plenty of plants, grasses, mosses, and beautiful flowers in summer—growing, too, close beside ice-fields that remain unmelted all the year round. But there is not a tree large enough to make a harpoon of. Consequently the Eskimos are obliged to make sledges of bones; and as the bones and tusks of the walrus are not big enough for this purpose, they tie and piece them together in a remarkably neat and ingenious manner.

Sometimes, indeed, they find pieces of drift-wood in the sea. Wrecks of whale-ships, too, are occasionally found by the natives in the south of Greenland. A few pieces of the precious wood obtained in this way are exchanged from one tribe to another, and so find their way north. But the further north we go the fewer pieces of this kind of wood do we find; and in the far north, where our adventurous voyagers were now ice-bound, the Eskimos have very little wood, indeed.

Food is the chief object which the Eskimo has in view when he goes out to do battle with the walrus. Its flesh is somewhat coarse, no doubt, but it is excellent, nourishing food notwithstanding, and although a well-fed Englishman might turn up his nose at it, many starving Englishmen have smacked their lips over walrus-beef in days gone by—aye, and have eaten it raw, too, with much delight!

Let not my reader doubt the truth of this. Well-known and truth-loving men have dwelt for a time in those regions, and some of these have said that they actually came to *prefer* the walrus flesh raw, because it was more strengthening, and fitted them better for undertaking long and trying journeys in extremely cold weather. One of the most gallant men who ever went to the Polar seas, (Dr. Kane, of the American navy), tells us, in his delightful book, "Arctic Explorations", that he frequently ate raw flesh and liked it, and that the Eskimos often eat it raw. In fact, they are not particular. They will eat it cooked or raw—just as happens to be most convenient for them.

When the animals, whose killing I have described, were secured, the Eskimos proceeded to skin and cut them up. The sailors, of course, assisted, and learned a lesson. While this was going on one of their number went away for a short time, and soon returned with a sledge drawn by about a dozen dogs. This they loaded with the meat and hide of the bull, intending evidently to leave the cow to their new friends, as being their property. But Gregory thought they were entitled to a share of it, so, after loading his sledge with a considerable portion of the meat, he gave them the remainder along with the hide.

This pleased them mightily, and caused them to talk much, though to little purpose. However, Gregory made good use of the language of signs. He also delighted them with the gift of a brass ring, an old knife, and a broken pencil-case, and made them understand that his abode was not far distant, by drawing the figure of a walrus in a hole in the snow, and then a thing like a bee-hive at some distance from it, pointing northward at the same time. He struck a harpoon into the outline of the walrus, to show that it was the animal that had just been killed, and then went and lay down in the picture of the bee-hive, to show that he dwelt there.

The natives understood this quite well. They immediately drew another bee-hive, pointed to the south and to the sun, and held up five fingers. From this it was understood that their village was five days distant from the spot where they then were.

He next endeavored to purchase three of their dogs, but they objected to this, and refused to accept of three knives as a price for them. They were tempted, however, by the offer of a whale harpoon and a hemp line, and at last agreed to let him have three of their best dogs. This the young doctor considered a piece of great good fortune, and being afraid that they would repent, he prepared to leave the place at once. The dogs were fastened by lines to the sledge of their new masters. A whip was made out of a strip of walrus hide, a bone served for a handle, and away they went for the brig at a rattling pace, after bidding the natives farewell, and making them understand that they hoped to meet again in the course of the winter.

Thus happily ended their first meeting with the Eskimos. It may well be believed that there were both astonishment and satisfaction on board the *Hope* that night, when the hunting party returned, much sooner than had been expected, with the whip cracking, the men cheering, the dogs howling, and the sledge well laden with fresh meat.

Chapter VIII

THE CAUSE OF ICE-BERGS—FOX-CHASE—A BEAR.

One day, long after the walrus-hunt just described, Joe Davis stood on the deck of the *Hope*, leaning over the side and looking out to sea—at least in the direction of the sea, for, although mid-day, it was so dark that he could not see very far in any direction. Joe was conversing with Mr. Dicey on the appearance of things around him.

"Do you know, Mr. Dicey," said he, "wot it is as causes them there ice-bergs?"

Mr. Dicey looked very grave and wise for a few seconds without answering. Then he said, in rather a solemn tone, "Well, Davis, to tell you the real truth, I don't know!"

Now, as this question is one of considerable interest, I shall endeavour to answer it for the benefit of the reader.

The whole of the interior of Greenland is covered with ice and snow. This snowy covering does not resemble that soft snow which falls on our own hills. It is hard, and *never* melts entirely away. The snow there is in some places a thousand feet thick! It covers all the hill-tops and fills up all the valleys, so that the country may be said to be a buried land. Since the world began, perhaps, snow has been falling on it every winter; but the summers there have been so short that they could not melt away the snow of one winter before that of another came and covered it up and pressed it down. Thus, for ages, the snow of one year has been added to that which was left of the preceding, and the pressure has been so great that the mass has been squeezed nearly as hard as pure ice.

The ice that has been formed in this way is called *glacier*, and the glaciers of Greenland cover, as I have said, the whole country, so that it can never be cultivated or inhabited by man unless the climate change. There are glaciers of this kind in many other parts of the world. We have them in Switzerland and in Norway, but not on nearly so large a scale as in Greenland.

Now, although this glacier-ice is clear and hard, it is not quite so solid as pure ice, and when it is pushed down into the valleys by the increasing masses above it, actually *flows*. But this flowing motion cannot be seen. It is like the motion of the hour hand of a watch, which cannot be perceived however closely it may be looked at. You might go to one of the valleys of Greenland and gaze at a glacier for days together, but you would see no motion whatever. All would appear solid, frozen up, and still. But notice a block of stone lying on the surface of the glacier, and go back many months after and you will find the stone lying a little further down the valley than when you first saw it. Thus glaciers are formed and thus they slowly move. But what has all this to do with ice-bergs? We shall see.

As the great glaciers of the north, then, are continually moving down the valleys, of course their ends are pushed into the sea. These ends, or tongues, are often hundreds of feet thick. In some places they present a clear glittering wall to the sea of several hundreds of feet in height, with perhaps as much again lost to view down in the deep water. As the extremities of these tongues are shoved farther and farther out they chip off and float away. *These chips are ice-bergs!* I have already said that ice-bergs are sometimes miles in extent—like islands; that they sink seven or eight hundred feet below the surface, while their tops rise more than a hundred feet above it—like mountains. If these, then, are the "chips" of the Greenland glaciers, what must the "old blocks" be?

Many a long and animated discussion the sailors had that winter in the cabin of the *Hope* on the subject of ice and ice-bergs!

When the dark nights drew on, little or nothing could be done outside by our voyagers, and when the ice everywhere closed up, all the animals forsook them except polar bears, so that they ran short of fresh provisions. As months of dreary darkness passed away, the scurvy, that terrible disease, began to show itself among the men, their bodies became less able to withstand the cold, and it was difficult for them at last to keep up their spirits. But they fought against their troubles bravely.

Captain Harvey knew well that when a man's spirits go he is not worth much. He therefore did his utmost to cheer and enliven those around him.

One day, for instance, he went on deck to breathe a mouthful of fresh air. It was about eleven in the forenoon, and the moon was shining brightly in the clear sky. The stars, too, and the aurora borealis, helped to make up for the total absence of the sun. The cold air cut like a knife against his face when he issued from the hatchway, and the cold nose of one of the dogs immediately touched his hand, as the animal gambolled round him with delight; for the extreme severity of the weather began to tell on the poor dogs, and made them draw more lovingly to their human companions.

"Ho! hallo!" shouted the captain down the hatchway. "A fox-chase! a fox-chase! Tumble up, all hands!"

The men were sitting at the time in a very dull and silent mood. They were much cast down, for as it had been cloudy weather for some weeks past, thick darkness had covered them night and day, so that they could not tell the one from the other, except by the help of their watches, which were kept carefully going. Their journals, also, were written up daily, otherwise they must certainly have got confused in their time altogether!

In consequence of this darkness the men were confined almost entirely to the cabin for a time. Those who had scurvy, got worse; those who were well, became gloomy. Even Pepper, who was a tremendous joker, held his tongue, and Joe Davis, who was a great singer, became silent. Jim Crofts was in his bunk "down" with the scurvy, and stout Sam Baker, who was a capital teller of stories, could not pluck up spirit enough to open his mouth. "In fact," as Mr. Dicey said, "they all had a most 'orrible fit o' the blues!" The captain and officers were in better health and spirits than the men, though they all fared alike at the same table, and did the same kind of work, whatever that might chance to be. The officers, however, were constantly exerting themselves to cheer the men, and I have no doubt that this very effort of theirs was the means of doing good to themselves. "He that watereth others shall be watered," says the Word of God. I take this to mean— he that does good to others shall get good to himself.

So it certainly was with the officers of the *Hope*.

When the captain's shout reached the cabin Jim Crofts had just said: "I'll tell 'ee what it is, messmates, if this here state of things goes on much longer, I'll go out on the floes, walk up to the first polar bear I meet, and ask him to take his supper off me!"

There was no laugh at this, but Pepper remarked, in a quiet way, that "he needn't put himself to so much trouble, for he was such a pale-faced, disagreeable looking object that no bear would eat him unless it was starving."

"Well, then, I'll offer myself to a starvin' bear—to one that's a'most dead with hunger," retorted Jim gloomily.

"What's that the cap'en is singin' out?" said Davy Butts, who was mending a pair of canvas shoes.

The men roused themselves at once; for the hope of anything new turning up excited them.

"Hallo! ho!" roared the captain again, in a voice that might have started a dead walrus. "Tumble up, there!—a fox-chase! I'll give my second-best fur-coat to the man that catches foxey!"

In one instant the whole crew were scrambling up

the ladder. Even Jim Crofts, who was really ill, rolled out of his bunk and staggered on deck, saying he would have a "go after foxey if he should die for it!"

The game of fox is simple. One man is chosen to be the fox. He runs off and the rest follow. They are bound to go wherever the fox leads. In this case it was arranged that the fox should run round the deck until he should be caught; then the man who caught him should become fox, and continue running on with all the rest following, until he, in turn, should be caught, and so on until the one who could run longest and fastest should break down all the rest. The warm fur-coat was a prize worth running for in such a cold climate, so the game began with spirit. Young Gregory offered to be fox first, and away they went with a yell. Mr. Mansell was a little lame, and soon gave in. Mr. Dicey fell at the second round, and was unable to recover distance. Gregory would certainly have gained the coat, for he was strong, and had been a crack racer at school; but he did not want the coat, so allowed Sam Baker to catch him. Sam held on like a deer for a few minutes, and one after another the men dropped off as they were blown. Jim Crofts, poor fellow, made a gallant burst, but his limbs refused to help his spirit. He fell, and was assisted below by the captain and replaced in his bunk, where, however, he felt the benefit of his efforts.

The race was now kept up by Sam Baker, Joe Davis, and Butts. These three were struggling on and panting loudly, while their comrades danced about, clapped their mittened hands, and shouted, "Now then, Sam!—go in and win, Joe!—Butts, forever!" and such-like encouraging cries.

To the surprise of everyone Davy Butts came off the winner, and for many a day after that enjoyed the warm coat which he said his long legs had gained for him.

This effort of the captain to cheer the men was very successful, so he resolved to follow it up with an attempt at private theatricals. Accordingly this thing was proposed and heartily agreed to. Next day everyone was busy making preparations. Tom Gregory agreed to write a short play. Sam Baker, being the healthiest man on board, was willing to act the part of an invalid old lady, and Jim Crofts consented to become a gay young doctor for that occasion.

Meanwhile the captain arranged a piece of real work, for he felt that the attempt to keep up the spirits alone would not do. They had been for a long time living on salt provisions. Nothing could restore the crew but fresh meat—yet fresh meat was not to be had. The walrus and deer were gone, and although foxes and bears were still around them, they had failed in all their attempts to shoot or trap any of these animals. A visit to the Eskimo camp, therefore, (if such a camp really existed), became necessary; so, while the theatricals were in preparation, a small sledge was rigged up, Gregory and Sam Baker were chosen to go with him; the dogs were harnessed, and, on a fine, starry forenoon, away they went to the south at full gallop, with three hearty cheers from the crew of the brig, who were left in charge of the first mate.

The journey thus undertaken was one full of risk. It was not known how far distant the natives might be, or where they were likely to be found. The weather was intensely cold. Only a small quantity of preserved meat could be taken—for the rest, they trusted in some measure to their guns. But the captain's great hope was to reach the Eskimo village in a day or two at the farthest. If he should fail to do so, the prospect of himself and his crew surviving the remainder of the long winter was, he felt, very gloomy indeed.

Success attended this expedition at the very beginning. They had only been eight hours out when they met a bear sitting on its haunches behind a hummock. "Hallo! look out!" cried Gregory, on catching sight of him. "Fire, lads," said the captain, "I'm not quite ready." Gregory fired and the bear staggered. Baker then fired and it fell!

This was a blessing which filled their hearts so full of thankfulness that they actually shook hands with each other, and then gave vent to three hearty cheers. Their next thoughts were given to their comrades in the *Hope*.

"You and Baker will camp here, Tom," said the captain, "and I will return to the brig with a sledge-load of the meat. When I've put it aboard I'll come straight back to you. We'll keep a ham for ourselves, of course. Now then, to work."

To work the three men went. A hind leg of the bear was cut off, the rest was lashed firmly on the sledge, and the dogs enjoyed a feed while this was being done.

Then the captain cracked his whip. "Good-bye, lads," "Good-bye, captain," and away he and the dogs and sledge went, and were soon lost to view among the hummocks of the frozen sea.

Chapter IX

The proceedings of this sledge party were so interesting that I give them in the words of Tom Gregory's journal:

"*Sunday.*—We have indeed cause to rejoice and to thank God for His mercies this morning. Last night we shot a bear, and the captain is away with the carcass of it to our poor scurvy-smitten friends in the *Hope*. This Sunday will be a real day of rest for me and Sam Baker, though our resting-place is a very queer one. After the captain left us, we looked about for a convenient place to encamp, and only a few yards from the spot where we killed the bear we found the ruins of an old Eskimo hut made partly of stones, partly of ice. We set to work to patch it up with snow, and made it perfectly air-tight in about two hours.

"Into this we carried our bear-skins and things, spread them on the snowy floor, put a lump of bear's fat into our tin travelling lamp, and prepared supper. We were not particular about the cookery. We cut a couple of huge slices off our bear's ham, half roasted them over the lamp, and began. It was cut, roast, and come again, for the next hour and a half. I positively never knew what hunger was until I came to this savage country! And I certainly never before had any idea of how much I could eat at one sitting!

"This hearty supper was washed down with a swig of melted snow-water. We had some coffee with us, but were too tired to infuse it. Then we blocked up the door with snow, rolled our bear-skins round us, and were sound asleep in five minutes.

"Lucky for us that we were so careful to stop up every hole with snow, for, during the night the wind rose and it became so intensely cold that Baker and I could scarcely keep each other warm enough to sleep, tired though we were. At this moment my fingers are so stiff that they will hardly hold the pencil with which I write, and the gale is blowing so furiously outside that we dare not open the door. This door, by the way, is only a hole big enough to creep through. The captain cannot travel to-day. He knows we are safe, so I will not expect him. I have brought my small Testament with me. It has hitherto been my constant travelling companion. I am thus provided with mental food. But, in truth, I shall not want much of that for the next twelve hours. Rest! rest! rest! is what we require. No one can imagine how a man can enjoy rest, after he has been for many months exposed to constant, exhausting, heart-breaking toil, with the thermometer *always* below zero, and with nothing but salt food to keep him alive.

"*Tuesday night.*—Here we are at last—among the Eskimos! and what a queer set they are, to be sure. All fat and fur! They look as broad as they are long. They wear short fox and seal-skin coats, or shirts, with hoods to then; no trousers, but long boots, that come up and meet the coats. Women, men, and babies, all dressed alike, or nearly so. The only difference is that the women's boots are longer and wider than those of the men. But I forgot—yes, there is one other difference; the women have *tails* to their coats; the men have none! Real tails—not like the broad skirts of our dress-coats, but long, narrow tails, something like the tail of a cow, with a broadish flap at the end of it. This they evidently look upon as a handsome ornament, for I observe that when they go off on a journey, each woman buttons her tail up to her waist, to keep it out of the way, and when she returns she unbuttons it, and comes into camp with her tail flowing gracefully behind her!

"We had a terrible journey of it down here. The captain returned to us on Monday morning early, and the next two days we spent struggling over the hummocks and out upon the floes. It was so cold that the wind cut into our very marrow. We have all had our faces frozen, more or less, but not badly. Baker will have an ugly spot on the end of his nose for some weeks to come. It is getting black now, and as the nose itself is bright red and much swelled, his appearance is not improved. I foolishly tried to eat a little snow yesterday morning, and the consequence is that my lips are sore and bloody. On Monday afternoon the dogs and sledge went head over heels into a deep rut in the ice, and it cost us two hours to get them out again. Luckily no damage was done, although the captain was on the sledge at the time.

"We had almost despaired of finding the village when we came upon a sledge track that led us straight up to it. I shall never forget the beauty of the scene on our arrival. The sky was lighted up with the most beautiful aurora I have yet seen in these regions. Stars spangled the sky in millions. Great ice-bergs rose in wild confusion in the distance, and all along the shore for a few hundred yards were clusters of snow-huts. They looked exactly like bee-hives. I have seen many a strange house, but the strangest of all is certainly a house of snow! To-day I was fortunate enough to see one built. It was done very neatly. The hard snow was cut into slabs with a wooden knife. These were piled one above another in regular order, and cemented with snow—as bricks are with lime. The form of the wall was circular, and the slabs were so shaped that they sloped inwards, thus forming a dome, or large bee-hive, with a key-stone slab in the top to keep all firm. A hole was then cut in the side for a door—just large enough to admit of a man creeping through. In front of this door a porch or passage of snow was built. The only way of getting into the hut is by creeping on hands and knees along the passage. A hole was also cut in the roof, into which was inserted a piece of clear ice, to serve for a window.

"The natives received us with wild surprise, and I found my old friends, the walrus-hunters, among them. They were remarkably friendly. One stout, middle-aged fellow invited us to his hut. I am now seated in it beside the Eskimo's wife, who would be a good-looking woman if she were not so fat, dirty, and oily! But we cannot expect people living in this fashion, and in such a country, to be very clean. Although the hut is white outside, it is by no means white inside. They cook all their food over an oil-lamp, which also serves to heat the place; and it is wonderful how warm a house of snow becomes. The cold outside is so great as to prevent the walls melting inside. Besides Myouk, our host, and his wife, there are two of the man's sisters, two lads, two girls, and a baby in the hut. Also six dogs. The whole of them—men, women, children, and dogs, are as fat as they can be, for they have been successful in walrus-hunting of late. No wonder that the perspiration is running down my face! The natives feel the heat, too, for they are all half-naked—the baby entirely so; but they seem to like it!

"What a chattering, to be sure! I am trying to take notes, and Myouk's wife is staring at me with her mouth wide open. It is a wonder she can open her eyes at all, her cheeks are so fat. The captain is trying, by the language of signs, to get our host to understand that we are much in want of fresh meat. Sam Baker is making himself agreeable to the young people, and the plan he has hit upon to amuse them is to show them his watch, and let them hear it tick. Truly, I have seldom seen a happier family group than this Eskimo household, under their snowy roof!

"There is to be a grand walrus-hunt to-morrow. We shall accompany them, and see whether our endurance on a long march, and our powers with the rifle, cannot impress them with some respect for us. At present they have not much. They seem to think us a pale-faced set of helpless creatures.

"*Wednesday night.*—We have just returned from the

hunt; and a tremendous hunt it was! Six walrus and two bears have been killed, and the whole village is wild with delight. Cooking is going on in every hut. But they have no patience. Nearly everyone is munching away at a lump of raw walrus flesh. All their faces are more or less greasy and bloody. Even Myouk's baby—though not able to speak—is choking itself with a long, stringy piece of blubber. The dogs, too, have got their share. An Eskimo's chief happiness seems to be in eating, and I cannot wonder at it, for the poor creatures have hard work to get food, and they are often on the verge of starvation.

"What a dirty set they are! I shall never forget the appearance of Myouk's hut when we entered it this evening after returning from the hunt. The man's wife had made the wick of her stone lamp as long as possible in order to cook a large supper. There were fifteen people crowded together in this hive of snow, and the heat had induced them to throw off the greater part of their clothing. Every hand had a greasy lump of bear or walrus meat in it; every mouth was in full occupation, and every fat face, of man, woman, and child, was beaming with delight and covered with dirt and oil!

"The captain and I looked at each other and smiled as we entered, and Sam Baker laughed outright. This set all the natives laughing, too. We did not much relish the idea of supping and sleeping in such a place—but necessity has no law. We were hungry as hawks, desperately tired, and the temperature outside is 35 degrees below zero. The first duty of the night is now over. We have supped. The natives will continue to eat the greater part of the night. They eat till they fall asleep; if they chance to awake they eat again. Half of them are asleep now, and snoring. The other half are eating slowly, for they are nearly full. The heat and smell are awful! I am perspiring at every pore. We have taken off as much of our clothes as decency will permit. Sam has on a pair of trousers—nothing more. I am in the same state! There is little room, as may be supposed. We have to lie huddled up as we best can, and a strange sight we are as the red light of the flaring lamp falls on us. At this moment Myouk's wife is cutting a fresh steak. The youngest boy is sound asleep with a lump of fat between his teeth. The captain is also sound, with his legs sprawling over the limbs of half a dozen slumbering natives. He is using the baby as a pillow. It is curious to think that these poor creatures always live in this way. Sometimes feasting, sometimes starving. Freezing out on the floes; stewing under their roofs of snow. Usually fat; for the most part jolly; always dirty!

"It is sad, too, to think of this; for it is a low condition for human beings to live in. They seem to have no religion at all. Certainly none that is worthy of the name. I am much puzzled when I think of the difficulties in the way of introducing Christianity among these northern Eskimos. No missionary could exist in such a climate and in such circumstances. It is with the utmost difficulty that hardy seamen can hold out for a year, even with a ship-load of comforts. But this is too deep a subject to write about to-night! I can't keep my eyes open. I will, therefore, close my note-book and lie down to sleep—perhaps to be suffocated! I hope not!"

Accordingly, our young friend the doctor did lie down to sleep, and got through the night without being suffocated. Indeed, he slept so soundly that Captain Harvey could scarcely rouse him next morning.

"Hallo! Tom! Tom!" cried he loudly, at the same

ESKIMO VILLAGE —Page 274

time shaking his nephew's arm violently.

"Aye, eh!" and a tremendous yawn from Tom. "What now, uncle? Time to rise, is it? Where am I?"

"Time to rise!" replied the captain, laughing. "I should think it is. Why, it's past eleven in the forenoon. The stars are bright and the sky clear. The aurora, too, is shining. Come, get up! The natives are all outside watching Sam while he packs our sledge. The ladies are going about the camp whisking their tails and whacking their babies in great glee, for it is not every day they enjoy such a feed as they had last night."

In half an hour they were ready. The whole village turned out to see them start. Myouk, with his wife Oomia, and the baby, and his son Meetek, accompanied them to Refuge Harbour. Oomia's baby was part of herself. She could not move without it! It was always naked, but being stuffed into the hood of its mother's fur-coat, it seemed always warm.

"I say, Tom, what's that up in the sky?" said Captain Harvey suddenly, after they had been driving for a couple of hours. "It's the strangest looking thing I ever did see."

"So it is," replied Gregory, gazing intently at the

object in question, which seemed high up in the air. "It can't be a comet, because it gives no light."

"Perhaps not, but it has got a tail, that's a fact," said Baker, in a voice of surprise. "Who ever heard of a dark, four-cornered star with a tail? If I had seen it in daylight, and in Merry England, I would have said it was a kite!"

"A kite! nonsense," cried the captain; "what in the world *can* it be?"

Reader, you shall find that out in the next chapter.

Chapter X

When Mr. Mansell was left in charge of the brig a heavy weight lay on his heart, and he could by no means take part in the preparations for the theatricals which occupied the rest of the crew. He felt that life or death depended on the success of the captain in his search for fresh meat. Already most of the men were ill with scurvy, and some of them were alarmingly low. Nothing could save them but fresh meat, and when the first mate thought of the difficulties and dangers of a journey on the floes in such weather, and the uncertainty of the Eskimos being discovered, his heart misgave him.

About an hour after the departure of Captain Harvey on the Monday morning he took Davy Butts aside.

"Davy," said he, "you've been at work on these kites a long time. Are they nearly finished?"

"Quite finished, sir," answered Butts.

"Then get them up, for there is a good breeze. I shall try them on our small sledges. It will at least stir up and amuse the men."

Ten minutes after this the crew were summoned on deck to witness an experiment. A small dog sledge lay on the hard snow beside the vessel, and near to this Davy Butts and Mr. Dicey were holding on to a stout line, at the end of which an enormous kite was pulling.

This kite was square in shape, made of the thickest brown paper, and nearly six feet across. That its power was great was evident from the difficulty with which the two men held it. The end of the line was fastened to the sledge.

"Now, boys, ease off line till it is taut, and then wait for the word," said Davy Butts, jumping on to the sledge. "Now! Let go!"

Away went the sledge over the hard snow at the rate of three miles an hour, which soon increased to double that rate. Davy cheered and waved his arms. The men gave one loud "hurrah" of surprise and delight, and set off in mad pursuit. They were soon left behind. "Hold on, Davy!" "Good-bye, Butts." "Look out, mind the ridge!"

The last warning was needful. The sledge was rushing furiously toward a long ridge of ice which rose in a sharp slope to a height of three feet, and descended on the other side to an equal depth, but without any slope. Davy saw his danger, but he did not dare to put out foot or hand to check his progress. Even if he had it would have been of no use. Up the slope he went as a sea-gull skims over a wave; for one moment he was in the air—the next, he came down with a crash that nearly dislocated all his joints, and his teeth came together with a loud snap. (By good fortune his tongue was not between them!) The sledge was a strong one, and the thing was done so quickly and neatly that it did not upset. But now a large and rugged hummock lay right before him. To go against that would have been certain death, so Davy made up his mind at once, and jumped off at the smoothest part of the floe he could find. The lightened sledge sprang away like a rocket, and was brought up with a sudden jerk by the hummock.

Of course the line broke, and the kite commenced to descend. It twirled and circled violently round, and at last went crash into an ice-berg, where it was broken to pieces!

"Not so bad for a beginning," said Mansell, as poor Davy came back, looking very crest-fallen. "Now, Butts, come below. You have proved that the thing will do. Mr. Dicey, get yourself ready for a trip over the ice. Let three men prepare to accompany you. I shall send you off to-morrow."

Dicey, much surprised, went off to obey these orders; and Mansell, with the assistance of Butts, fitted the second kite for the intended journey. He made a rough guess at the strength of its pull, and loaded the sledge accordingly. Two tail ropes were fastened to the last bar of the sledge for the men to hold on by and check its speed. A sort of anchor was made by which it could be stopped at any moment, and two stout poles, with iron claws at the end of them, were prepared for scraping over the snow and checking the pace.

Next day all was ready. A trial was made and the thing found to work admirably. The trial trip over, they bade their comrades farewell, and away they went due south, in the direction where the native village was supposed to be.

It was this remarkable tow-horse that had filled Captain Harvey and his companions with so much surprise. The appearance of the sledge immediately after, with a shout and a cheer from Dicey and the men, explained the mystery.

Being so near the Eskimo camp they at once returned to it, in order to allow the newly arrived party to rest, as well as to load their sledge with as much fresh meat as it could carry; for which supplies the captain took care to pay the natives with a few knives and a large quantity of hoop-iron—articles that were much more valuable to them than gold. As the wind could not be made to turn about to suit their convenience, the kite was brought down and given to Davy to carry, and a team of native dogs were harnessed to the sledge instead. On the following day the united party set out on their return to the brig, which they reached in safety.

Tom Gregory's account of the Eskimos who accompanied them to their wooden home is amusing. His journal runs thus:

"The amazement of our visitors is very great. Myouk, his wife and baby, and his son Meetek, are now our guests. When they first came in sight of the brig they uttered a wild shout—the men did so, at least—and tossed their arms and opened their eyes and mouths. They have never shut them since. They go all round the vessel, staring and gaping with amazement. We have given them a number of useful presents, and intend to send them home loaded with gifts for their friends. It is necessary to make a good impression on them. Our lives depend very much on the friendship of these poor people. We find that they are terrible thieves. A number of knives and a hatchet were missed—they were found hidden in Myouk's sledge. We tried to prevail on Oomia to sell her long boots. To our surprise she was quite willing to part with *one*, but nothing would induce her to give up the *other*. One of the men observed her steal a knife out of the cabin and hide it in the leg of her boot. The reason was now plain. We pulled off the boot without asking leave, and found there a large assortment of articles stolen from us. Two or three knives, a spoon, a bit of hoop-iron, and a marline spike. I have tried to make them understand, by signs, that this is very wicked conduct, but they only laugh at me. They are not in the least ashamed, and evidently regard stealing as no sin.

"We have shot a musk ox. There are many of these creatures in other parts of the Arctic regions, but this is the first we have seen here. He fell to my rifle, and is now being devoured by ourselves and our dogs with great relish. He is about the size of a very small cow; has a large head and enormously thick horns, which cover the whole top of his head, bend down toward his cheeks, and then curve up and outward at the point. He is covered with long, brown hair, which almost reaches the ground, and has no tail worthy of the name. He seems to be an active and an angry creature. When I wounded him he came at me furiously, but had not pluck to charge home. As he turned away I gave him the shot that killed him. The meat is not bad, but it smells strongly of musk. Walrus is better.

"Myouk and his son Meetek and I have had a most exciting bear-hunt since we returned. I followed these men one day, as I thought them bold, active-looking fellows, who would be likely to show me good Eskimo sport. And I was not disappointed.

"About two miles from the brig we came on fresh bear tracks. A glow of the aurora gave us plenty of light. 'What is yon round white lump?' thought I. 'A bear? No, it must be a snow-wreath!' Myouk did not think so, for he ran behind a lump of ice, and became excited. He made signs to me to remain there while he and his son should go and attack the bear. They were armed each with a long lance. I must say, when I remembered the size and strength of the polar bear, that I was surprised to find these men bold enough to attack him with such arms. I had my rifle, but determined not to use it except in case of necessity. I wished to see how the natives were accustomed to act.

"They were soon ready. Gliding swiftly from one lump of ice to another, they got near enough to make a rush. I was disobedient! I followed, and when the rush was made I was not far behind them. The bear was a very large one. It uttered an angry growl on seeing the men running toward it, and rose on its hind legs to receive them. It stood nearly eight feet high when in this position, and looked really a terrible monster. I stood still behind a hummock at a distance of about fifty yards, with my rifle ready.

"On coming close up the father and son separated, and approached the bear one on each side. This divided his attention, and puzzled him very much; for, when he made a motion as if he were going to rush at Myouk, Meetek flourished his spear, and obliged him to turn—then Myouk made a demonstration, and turned him back again. Thus they were enabled to get close to its side before it could make up its mind which to attack. But the natives soon settled the question for it. Myouk was on the bear's right side, Meetek on its left. The father pricked it with the point of his lance. A tremendous roar followed, and the enraged animal turned towards him. This was just what he wanted, because it gave the son an opportunity of making a deadly thrust.[1] Meetek was not slow to do it. He plunged his lance deep into the bear's heart, and it fell

1. See frontispiece

at once at full length, while a crimson stream poured out of the wound upon the snow.

"While this fight was going on I might have shot the animal through the heart with great ease, for it was quite near to me, and when it got up on its hind legs its broad chest presented a fine target. It was difficult to resist the temptation to fire, but I wished to see the native manner of doing the thing from beginning to end, so did not interfere. I was rewarded for my self-denial.

"Half an hour later, while we were dragging the carcass toward the brig, we came unexpectedly upon another bear. Myouk and Meetek at once grasped their lances and ran forward to attack him. I now resolved to play them a trick. Besides my rifle I carried a large horse-pistol in my belt. This I examined, and, finding it all right, I followed close at the heels of the Eskimos. Bruin got up on his hind legs as before, and the two men advanced close to him. I stopped when within thirty yards, cocked my rifle, and stood ready. Myouk was just going to thrust with his lance when—*bang!* went my rifle. The bear fell. It was shot right through the heart, but it struggled for some time after that. The natives seemed inclined to run away when they heard the shot, but I laughed and made signs of friendship. Then I went close up and shot the bear through the head with my pistol. This affair has filled my savage companions with deep respect for me!"

These two bears were the last they obtained that winter; but as a good supply of meat had been obtained from the Eskimos, they were relieved from anxiety for the time, and the health of the men began to improve a little. But this happy state of things did not last till spring. These sorely tried men were destined to endure much suffering before the light of the sun came back to cheer their drooping spirits.

Chapter XI

CHRISTMAS TIME—DEATH—RETURN OF LIGHT AND
HOPE—DISASTERS AND FINAL DELIVERANCE.

Christmas came at last, but with it came no bright sun to remind those ice-bound men of our Saviour—the "Sun of Righteousness"—whose birth the day commemorated. It was even darker than usual in Refuge Harbour on that Christmas-day. It was so dark at noon that one could not see any object more than a few yards distant from the eyes. A gale of wind from the nor'-west blew the snow-drift in whirling ghost-like clouds round the *Hope*, so that it was impossible to face it for a moment. So intense was the cold that it felt like sheets of fire being driven against the face! Truly it was a day well fitted to have depressed the heartiest of men. But man is a wonderful creature, not easy to comprehend! The very things that ought to have cast down the spirits of the men of the *Hope* were the things that helped to cheer them.

About this time, as I have said, the health of the crew had improved a little, so they were prepared to make the most of everything. Those feelings of kindliness and good-will which warm the breasts of all right-minded men at this season of the year, filled our Arctic voyagers to overflowing. Thoughts of "home" came crowding on them with a power that they had not felt at other times. Each man knew that on this day, more than any other day of that long, dark winter, the talk round a well-known hearth in Merry England would be of one who was far, far away in the dark regions of ice and snow. A tear or two that could not be forced back tumbled over rough cheeks which were not used to *that* kind of salt water; and many a silent prayer went up to call down a blessing on the heads of dear ones at home.

It blew "great guns outside," as Baker said, but what of that? it was a dead calm in the cabin! It was dark as a coal-hole on the floes. What then? it was bright as noon-day in the *Hope*! No sun blazed through the skylight, to be sure, but a lamp, filled with fat, glared on the table, and a great fire of coal glowed in the stove. Both of these together did not make the place too warm, but there were fur-coats and trousers and boots to help defy the cold. The men were few in number and not likely to see many friends on that Christmas-day. All the more reason why they should make the most of each other! Besides, they were wrong in their last idea about friends, for it chanced, on that very day, that Myouk the Eskimo paid them a visit—quite ignorant of its being Christmas, of course. Meetek was with him, and so was Oomia, and so was the baby—that remarkably fat, oily, naked baby, that seemed rather to enjoy the cold than otherwise!

They had a plum-pudding that day. Butts said it was almost as big as the head of a walrus. They had also a roast of beef—walrus-beef, of course—and first-rate it was. But before dinner the captain made them go through their usual morning work of cleaning, airing, making beds, posting journals, noting temperatures, opening the fire-hole, and redding up. For the captain was a great believer in the value of discipline. He knew that no man enjoys himself so much as he who has got through his work early—who has done his duty. It did not take them long, and when it was done the captain said, "Now, boys, we must be jolly to-day. As we can't get out we must take some exercise indoors. We shall need extra appetite to make away with that plum-pudding."

So, at it they went! Every sort of game or feat of strength known to sailors was played, or attempted. It was in the middle of all this that Myouk and his family arrived, so they were compelled to join. Even the fat baby was put into a blanket and swung round the cabin by Jim Croft, to the horror of its mother, who seemed to think it would be killed, and to the delight of its father, who didn't seem to care whether it was killed or not.

Then came the dinner. What a scene that was, to be sure! It would take a whole book to describe all that was said and done that day. The Eskimos ate till they could hardly stand—that was their usual custom. Then they lay down and went to sleep—that was their usual custom, too. The rest ate as heartily, poor fellows, as was possible for men not yet quite recovered from scurvy. They had no wine, but they had excellent coffee, and with this they drank to absent friends, sweethearts, and wives, and many other toasts, the mere mention of which raised such strong home-feelings in their breasts that some of them almost choked in the attempt to cheer. Then came songs and stories—all of them old, very old indeed—but they came out on this occasion as good as new. The great event of the evening, however, was a fancy ball, in which our friends Butts, Baker, Gregory, and Pepper distinguished themselves. They had a fiddle, and Dawkins the steward could play it. He knew nothing but Scotch reels; but what could have been better? They could all dance, or, if they could not, they all tried. Myouk and Meetek were made to join and they capered as gracefully as polar bears, which animals they strongly resembled in their hairy garments. Late in the evening came supper. It was just a repetition of dinner, with the remains of the pudding fried in bear's grease.

Thus passed Christmas-Day; much in the same way passed New Year's Day. Then the men settled down to their old style of life; but the time hung so heavy on their hands that their spirits began to sink again. The long darkness became intolerable and the fresh meat began to fail. Everything with life seemed to have forsaken the place. The captain made another trip to the Eskimo village and found the huts empty— the whole race had flown, he knew not whither! The private theatricals were at first very successful; but by degrees they lost their interest and were given up. Then a school was started and Gregory became head master. Writing and arithmetic were the only branches taught. Some of the men were much in need of instruction, and all of them took to the school with energy and much delight. It lasted longer than the theatricals did. As time wore on the fresh meat was finished, scurvy became worse; and it was as much as the men who were not quite knocked down could do to attend to those who were. Day after day Tom and Gregory and Sam Baker went out to hunt, and each day returned empty-handed. Sometimes an Arctic hare or a fox was got; but not often. At last rats were eaten as food. These creatures swarmed in the hold of the brig. They were caught in traps and shot with a bow and a blunt-headed arrow. But few of the men would eat them. The captain urged them to do so in vain. Those who did eat kept in better health than those who did not.

At last death came. Mr. Mansell sank beneath the terrible disease and was buried on the island. No grave could be dug in that hard frozen soil. The burial service was read by his sorrowing comrades over his body, which was frozen quite hard before they reached the grave, and then they laid it in a tomb of ice.

Time hung heavier than ever after that. Death is at all time a terrible visitant, but in such a place and under such circumstances it was tenfold more awful than usual. The blank in so small a band was a great one. It would perhaps have depressed them more than it did had their own situation been less desperate. But they had too fierce a battle to fight with disease, and the midnight gloom, and the bitter frost, to give way to much feeling about him who was gone.

Thus the long winter passed heavily away.

The sun came back at last, and when he came his beams shone upon a pale, shattered, and heart-weary band of men. But with his cheering light came also *hope*, and health soon followed in his train. Let young Gregory's journal tell the rest of our story, little of which now remains to be told.

"*February 21st.*—I have to record, with joy and gratitude, that the sun shone on the peaks of the ice-bergs to-day. The first time it has done so since October last. By the end of this month we shall have his rays on deck. I climbed to the top of a berg and actually bathed in sunshine this forenoon! We are all quite excited by the event, some of us even look jolly. Ah! what miserable faces my comrades have! so pale, so thin! We are all as weak as water. The captain and I are the strongest. Baker is also pretty well. Crofts and Davis are almost useless, the rest being quite helpless. The captain cooks, Baker and I hunt, Crofts and Davis attend to the sick. Another month of darkness would have killed the half of us.

"*March 10th.*—I shot a bear to-day. It did my heart good to see the faces of the men when I brought them the news and a piece of the flesh! The cold is not quite so intense now. Our coldest day this year has been the 17th of January. The glass stood at 67 degrees below zero on that morning. What a winter we have had! I shudder when I think of it. But there is more cause to be anxious about what yet lies before us. A single bear will not last long. Many weeks must pass before we are free. In June we hope to be released from our ice-prison. Fresh meat we shall then have in abundance. With it strength will return, and then, if God permits, we shall attempt to continue our voyage northward. The captain is confident on the point of open water round the Pole. The men are game for anything in spite of their sad condition."

Thus wrote Gregory at that date. Many weeks later we find him writing as follows:

"*June 15th.*—Free at last! The ice has been breaking up out at sea for some time past. It gave way in Refuge Harbour yesterday, and we warped out in the night. Everything is ready to push north again. We have been feeding heartily for many weeks on walrus, seals, wild-fowl, and last, but not least, on some grasses which make bad greens, but they have put scurvy to flight. All the men are well and strong and fit for hard work—though nothing like what they were when we first came here. Could it be otherwise? There are some of us who will carry the marks of this winter to our graves.

The bright beautiful sunshine shines now, all day and all night, cheering our hearts and inspiring hope.

"*June 16th.*—All is lost! How little we know what a day may bring forth! Our good little brig is gone, and we are here on the ice without a thing in the world except the clothes on our backs. I have saved my note-book, which chanced to be in my breast-pocket when the nip took place. How awfully sudden it was! We now appreciate the wise forethought of Captain Harvey in sending the large boat to Forlorn-Hope Bay. This boat is our last and only hope. We shall have to walk forty miles before we reach it.

"Our brig went down at three o'clock this afternoon. We had warped out into the floes to catch a light breeze that was blowing outside. For some time we held on steadily to the northward, but had not got out of sight of our winter quarters when a stream of ice set down upon us and closed in all around. At first we thought nothing of this, having escaped so many dangers of the kind last autumn, but by degrees the pressure increased alarmingly. We were jammed against a great ice-field which was still fast to the shore. In a few moments the sides of our little vessel began to creak and groan loudly. The men laboured like tigers at the ice-poles, but in vain. We heard a loud report in the cabin. No one knows what it was, but I suppose it must have been the breaking of a large bolt. At any rate it was followed by a series of crashes and reports that left no doubt in our minds as to what was going on. The ice was cracking the brig as if she had been a nut-shell. 'Save yourselves, lads!' cried the captain. One or two of the men made a rush to the hatchway, intending to run below and save some of their things. I ran to the cabin-ladder in the hope of saving our log-book and journals, but we all started back in horror, for the deck at that moment burst open almost under our feet. I cast one glance down through the opening into the hold. That glance was sufficient. The massive timbers and beams were being crushed together, doubled up, split, and shivered, as if they had been rotten straws! In another moment I was on the ice, where the whole crew were assembled, looking on at the work of destruction in solemn silence.

"After bursting in the vessel's sides the ice eased off, and she at once began to settle down. We could hear the water rushing furiously into the hold.

Ten minutes later she was gone! Thus end our hopes of farther discovery, and we are now left to fight our way in an open boat to the settlements on the south coast of Greenland. We have little time to think. Prompt action must be our watchword now, if we would escape from this world of ice.

"*July 20th.*—I have not entered a line in this journal since our vessel was lost. Our work has been so severe, and our sufferings so great, that I have had no heart for writing. Our walk to the place where we left the boat was a hard one, but we were cheered by finding the boat all safe, and the provisions and stores just as we left them. There was not enough to last out the voyage, but we had guns and powder. It is in vain to attempt to describe the events of the last few weeks. Constant, and hard, and cold work—at the oars, with the ice-poles—warping, hauling, and shoving. Beset by ice; driving before storms; detained by thick fogs; often wet to the skin; always tired, almost starving— such has been our fate since that sad day when our brig went down. And yet I don't think there is one of our party who would not turn about on the spot and renew our voyage of discovery, if he only got a chance of going in a well-appointed vessel. As it is, we must push on. Home! home! is our cry now.

"*August 1st.*—We are now in clover, after having been reduced to think of roasting our shoes for breakfast. For three days last week we ate nothing at all. Our powder has been expended for some weeks past. On Monday we finished our last morsel of the gull that Pepper managed to bring down with a stone. Tuesday was a terrible day. The agony of hunger was worse than I had expected it to be. Nevertheless, we tried hard to cheer each other as we laboured at the oars. Our only hope was to fall in with natives. Signs of them were seen everywhere, and we expected to hear their shouts at every point of land we doubled. The captain suggested that we should try *shoe-soup* on Wednesday morning! He was more than half in earnest, but spoke as if he were jesting. Pepper cocked his ears as if there was some hope still of work for him to do in his own line. Jim Crofts pulled off his shoe, and, looking at it earnestly, wondered if the sole would make a very tough chop. We all laughed, but I cannot say that the laugh sounded hearty. On the Thursday I began to feel weak, but the pangs of hunger were not so bad.

Our eyes seemed very large and wolfish. I could not help shuddering when I thought of the terrible things that men have done when reduced to this state.

"That evening, as we rounded a point, we saw an Eskimo boy high on a cliff, with a net in his hand. He did not see us for some time, and we were so excited that we stopped rowing to watch him in breathless silence. Thousands of birds were flying round his head among the cliffs. How often we had tried to kill some of these with sticks and stones, in vain! The net he held was a round one, with a long handle. Suddenly he made a dashing sweep with it and caught two of the birds as they passed! We now saw that a number of dead birds lay at his feet. In one moment our boat was ashore and we scrambled up the cliffs in eager haste. The boy fled in terror, but before he was well out of sight every man was seated on a ledge of rock with a bird at his mouth, sucking the blood! Hunger like ours despises cookery! It was fortunate that there were not many birds, else we should have done ourselves harm by eating too much. I have eaten many a good meal in my life, but never one so sweet, or for which I was so thankful, as that meal of raw birds, devoured on the cliffs of Greenland!

"That night we reached the Eskimo village, where we now lie. We find that it is only two days' journey from this place to the Danish settlements. There we mean to get on board the first ship that is bound for Europe—no matter what port she sails for. Meanwhile we rest our weary limbs in peace, for our dangers are past, and—thanks be to God—we are saved."

.　　.　　.　　.　　.　　.

Reader, my tale is told. A little book cannot be made to contain a long story, else would I have narrated many more of the strange and interesting events that befell our adventurers during that voyage. But enough has been written to give some idea of what is done and suffered by those daring men who attempt to navigate the Polar seas.

THE END